C000095118

The Mud the Beer ar__

Contents

Acknowledgements

My thanks are due to John Goodier, in particular, for his encouragement and practical assistance over what seems the very long time this book has been in the making and also to Denis, Gordon, Gerry, Alan and Tony for their contributions.

Secondly I would like to mention the following rugby clubs which have, directly or indirectly, influenced the contents and which may be the places where some of the incidents took place:-

Baildon, Ballina, Blackburn, Burnage, Burnley, Calder Vale, Cheadle Hulme, Cleckheaton, Colne and Nelson, Fylde, Kirby Lonsdale, Law Society, Leigh, Lymm, Newton-le-Willows, North Ribblesdale, Nottingham University (All Stars), Old Bedians, Skipton, Sligo, Southport, Thornton Cleveleys, Tyldesley, (Upper) Wharfedale, Vickers, Westport, and Wigan Unionists.

In the third place my thanks go to all the mere mortals, especially, the ones I played with or against whilst all those who enjoyed a pint after a game of rugby deserve an equal mention with all those who enjoyed their rugby before a pint.

Last but not least thanks to all those who have put in and continue to put in unpaid hours and enthusiasm into the running of the game without whom there would have been no mere mortals and no book.

Author's Foreword

After I had written this book I asked a former team-mate to read it; he did and he said it wasn't bad in parts. I was greatly encouraged; he had written a book or two himself, a remarkable achievement for a front row forward, so I valued his opinion. At the same time his comment reminded me of my playing days; you know those odd occasions when you might have had an indifferent game (by your own high standards) and are trying not to let your disappointment with yourself interfere with your enjoyment of a pint or two in the clubhouse afterwards. At such times it is always comforting when a team-mate takes the trouble to come over and offer some words of encouragement, such as "at least you weren't as bad as you were last week".

Anyway my friend went on to ask me why I had written the book. (As his enquiry came via e-mail I had to take it at face value even if I wasn't sure if he was really wondering why I had bothered). He claimed other readers would want to know the answer to this question (I don't really know why) and he said I ought to put something in at the beginning of the book by way of explanation, a kind of apology in advance, I suppose. Stuck for an answer, I re-booted both my remaining brain cells and subjected myself to a rigorous examination of my motives. It was a waste of time. If there was a reason with any kind of rational foundation when I began writing I have forgotten what it was but it must have seemed like a good idea at the time.

What I can tell you is how it all started and whom to blame: some years ago the very same bloke who drew me, as a callow youth, into rugby's magic circle took it upon himself to start editing a club newsletter and, knowing I was easily put upon, asked me to contribute an article. That went down so well

5

that three years later I was asked to try again. After that there was no stopping me; over a period of six years the pen scarcely left my hand. Admittedly, it did spend most of the time hovering over the paper - and I'll say it now before some smart ass of my acquaintance, and I seem to know several, does: writing is not the only thing I am slow at. However, as you can imagine, over such a period of time whatever might have been in my mind at the beginning evolved and the end result became an attempt, through the medium of a part real, part imaginary rugby club called "The Vale" and the experiences of an average player[1], to take the essential components of the game, the endeavour on the field, the camaraderie off it and the humour which is ever present both on and off, and to reassemble them, not just in bite-sized pieces but into satisfyingly large episodes in order that the reader might re-live the fun and enjoyment of some good, old rugby days without having to put his boots on.

One thing I can say for definite is that when I started scribbling I did not have the RFU Injured Players' Foundation in mind. Like all good rugby matches this book is in two parts. I have to leave the field at half-time due to injury. Thankfully, it was nothing serious but not being able to play was not an easy thing to come to terms with. As I was writing the book - you don't want to think about serious injury when you are playing - my thoughts did turn to the less fortunate and I had the idea of making a donation to the IPF. In turn, they agreed to associate their name and logo with the book. But "one pound, one measly pound" you might say. Well, the economics of writing a book come as a shock. Printing costs and the large chunk which publishers and/or booksellers take do not leave much and in this

---

[1] *Gordon, of whom more later, once kindly credited me with being the most average player he had ever come across.*

context one pound is a solid figure and not just an unspecified, possibly meaningless, percentage. It is also a reasonable estimate of what half the profit is likely to amount to. (That is to say it is complete guesswork). However, my agreement with the IPF is that they get their one pound on each sale anyway and I stand any losses but if by some chance sales are more than are anticipated they will get 50% of the actual profit which, hopefully, will mean considerably more than a pound a copy.

On behalf of the IPF, Bill Beaumont, a real giant of the game on the field and, increasingly, off it, has contributed his own foreword which follows. (Bill is Captain of the IPF Ambassadors but, in my opinion, this has nothing whatsoever to do with the kind words he has to say about the book).

I am also very grateful to the Greenwoods, father and son who have made the following pithy but flattering comments:-

"The funniest and most accurate evocation of the real grass-roots game since The Art of Coarse Rugby."
J.R.H. Greenwood (England 1966-1969)

"The perfect antidote to the self-absorption of the international game."
Will Greenwood M.B.E (England 1997-2004, British and Irish Lions 1997-2005)

Many thanks also for the following contributions.

"Quite outstanding. The core values of our great sport, teamwork, respect, sportsmanship and, particularly, enjoyment are all well portrayed and served up with a large helping of humour."
John Owen MBE Past President of the RFU, Chairman of the RFU Injured Players Foundation.

"I wish he'd played as well as he's written this book."
Gordon. Past President Atrocities Adjudication Board, The Vale

"Hilarious in parts, nostalgic in others, enjoyable throughout, some golden days of amateur rugby are brought to life again in this book". Peter Hughes BEM - Former International Referee; Past President Lancashire County RFU; Past President Manchester & District Referees' Society; Past President Burnley RUFC. (Past most things, but still enjoying being part of the rugby family).

"The funniest book anyone ever read me." A.P. Forward

"I really enjoyed reading this book. It could easily be about the clubs I used to play for. Happy days!"
Neil Smith, Harlequins RFC (Pretoria), Vickers Armstrong RUFC Swindon, Past President South African Barbarians

Foreword on behalf of the RFU Injured Players' Foundation
by Bill Beaumont

The Mud the Beer and the Rugby is an amusing chronicle of a fictional but true to life junior rugby club back in the day. Undeterred by floods or the failure to raise a full team, players from "The Vale" enjoy "the less serious but equally important side of amateur rugby".

This is the piano playing generation, happy on a bog of a playing surface or around the bar sharing a pint or two. Never mind that the Corporation pitch still has lion dung on it from a visiting summer circus and ignore the rain hammering down "like long silver nails".

Many who once listened to Bill McLaren's commentaries will feel a surge of memory and enjoy a wry smile as these tales of mischief from rugby's folklore unfold into scenarios with which they will be familiar.

This book paints a great picture of the traditional rugby family, looking out for each other and enjoying the game. It's good to know that this spirit continues through the work of the RFU Injured Players Foundation; a charity that supports any player catastrophically injured playing rugby in England; and also works to prevent such injuries happening at all. It's a great cause, and I'm proud that this book is supporting it.

Bill Beaumont

RFU INJURED PLAYERS FOUNDATION

Supporting and protecting the rugby family

With your backing, we look after seriously injured players for life and help prevent future injuries through research and education.

In the 4 years since the IPF was launched:
We have given out over £3.9 million to support injured players:

Over £2.5 million has been raised, or received in donations over the four years

Why we need you to raise money to support the rugby family

Seriously Injured Players

We provide immediate and lifelong support for all seriously injured rugby union players, both amateur and professional, to support them in their time of need, and empower them to live a full and independent life. We need to raise an additional £1million over the next four years to fund more support such as: specialist wheelchairs, vehicle adaptations, house conversions, communication aids, work re-training courses, adapted sports equipment and respite opportunities.

Protecting Players

We fund research into the causes and outcomes of serious injury, identifying the best ways to prevent and treat them, and we fund and input into the training of rugby coaches, players, referees and volunteers to protect players from serious injury. By raising £500,000 over the next four years we can support the real grass roots of the game through helping them with funding for training and equipment. Raising this further, will enable us to invest even more into injury prevention research to help make our game safer.

Call to action

We aim to be there for every seriously injured player, whenever they may need our support. We must also continue to make research breakthroughs to make the game safer and improve the care of those injured. But we need everyone that loves our great game to get involved. 100% of your support goes directly to injured players and prevention research – because the RFU cover all our admin costs. Please help today.

How you can help

Donate - As the RFU cover our overhead costs, all donations received can go straight to supporting and protecting our rugby family.

Fundraise - Organising a club event, or a solo challenge can be great fun as well as financially rewarding!

Spread the word - Simply telling other members of the rugby family about the IPF and what it does really helps us get support to where it's needed.

Supporters of the IPF

PRINCE HARRY IS OUR PATRON

Our IPF Ambassador XV:

Bill Beaumont (Captain),Shaun Edwards, Will Greenwood

John Inverdale, Rob Andrew, Maggie Alphonsi, Brian Moore,

Olly Barkley, Jeff Probyn, Martin Bayfield, Andrew Barrow,

David Barnes, Matt Hampson, John Bentley, Simon Amor

Says Bill Beaumont, captain of the IPF Ambassadors XV

"I'm asking every member of the rugby family to work together as a team. With your support it's no exaggeration to say that we can make a huge difference."

Case Study Example

Let us introduce you to Sandbach RFC player, David Twemlow, his wife, Sarah and daughter Heather. After David's serious injury the IPF responded immediately and was there in the hospital to support him and his wife. When it was time for David to leave hospital, recognising that their home was totally unsuitable for him return to in a wheelchair, we made an initial £200,000 grant and subsequent grants to create a specially adapted home where David can enjoy as normal a life as possible with his family. We have also supported David in retraining for a new job.

Says Sarah

"I really don't believe that we would have got through without the IPF. We are back together as a family in a new bungalow adapted for David to get around in his wheelchair all funded by the IPF. All we can say, as a family, is a big thank you!"

In total there are currently 132 former players with injuries going back to the 1960s who receive help from the Injured Players Foundation. This charity exists to provide ongoing help and support to players from all levels of the game.

By purchasing this copy of **The Mud the Beer and the Rugby** you have already made a small contribution to the foundation as £ 1 from every copy sold is donated to the Foundation. Every little does help. If you wish to make a donation of your own or to get involved in fundraising please visit

www.rfu.ipf.org.uk

TEAM TALK

The captains of the teams I played for always believed actions spoke louder than words and so team talks were never lengthy affairs. I'm going to maintain that tradition.

I realise some of you will have already had a quick look at the back and seen that there are more than 200 pages to get through. I know it's a lot but do not let that put you off:. *You can do it*! The good thing is there is no time limit so you can just take it at your own pace; one friend of mine said he thought it was better not to rush it – just take it chapter by chapter with a breather or a beer or even a day or two in between. He was amazed how quickly full time seemed to come round. Also, if you are struggling don't feel you have to face it alone. It's a team game after all; my other friend got his wife to read the book to him: an example front row forwards generally may find useful to follow.

Please remember that for every copy sold at least £1will be donated to RFU Injured Players Foundation so if you enjoy reading this book tell everybody to buy it. (But don't lend them your copy – let them buy their own).

OK. That's it. Get out there and enjoy yourself.

Warm-up

What's in a name? Only the best was good enough for the club's founding fathers so they side-stepped the obvious choice. To shackle their club with the name of the nearest smoke-choked mill town would have lacked imagination. Their vision took them out wider to the open space. They chose "The Vale", a name which spoke of fresh, clean air, of lush, green grass and of a river flowing freely beneath rolling hills; a name which evoked the green and pleasant land of their birthright.

All that greenness and pleasantness came at a price. On a typical summer day in the valley the early morning mist would rise off the river to meet the heavy, black clouds as they tumbled down over the sombre hillsides and then long, silver nails would fire down relentlessly, pinning the grass down into the heavy soil. Now I am not saying that this caused the pitches to be muddy but whilst other rugby clubs employed a groundsman The Vale had a hippo-warden. Sadly, it was no use; they still sneaked in after dark and on his day off. They were never actually spotted by anyone who could swear not to have touched a drop, but you could see where they had been from the tell-tale signs they left behind: an ugly, blackened morass, fifteen yards wide of churned, heavy mud bordered the touch-lines. Towards the middle of the pitch, occasional blades of grass which had escaped the nibbling of the mighty molars, became visible to the naked eye, sometimes in clumps of as many as five; but here and there even this black sea of comparative tranquillity was pocked by craters where a hippo had indulged itself with a roll on its back, waving all four legs in the air. Pure joy: nothing quite like it.

Sometimes the warden would attempt to re-level the playing surface with the tractor and heavy roller but in this perilous exercise the timing was everything. If the ground was too wet, which it was usually from the end of September unless the winter rains had come early, the warden with his tractor and roller risked being lost for ever, entombed in treacle. If it was not too wet but not quite dry enough great pancakes of black, tacky mud would cling to the roller like giant claps left by the hippos after a serious night on the Guinness. In the worst case scenario the pitch would start to roll up behind the tractor like a massive black snowball. That was the first team pitch. The second team pitch was not quite in such good condition. It was called the second team pitch because, although the third team played on it one week and the fourth team the next, nobody wanted them to have an inferiority complex. I mean when you have gone to the trouble of calling the thirds "the Extra 'A' team" and the fourths "the 'B' team" you don't want to give the game away by telling them they are to play on the third/fourth team pitch; even rugby players could work that one out.

The first team pitch belonged to The Vale itself but the second team pitch belonged to the local authority. Just who had named this pitch "The Prairie" and the position of his/her tongue at the time is not recorded. Yet, as some literary fellow once remarked, "a rose by any other name . . .", and the home players were so used to that name that the mirth of visiting players as they heard it for the first time was not appreciated by the hosts and insulted pride encouraged The Vale lads to get stuck in right from the first whistle.

Before this pitch had become known as the second team pitch it had been simply "the pitch" for in those distant and sometimes difficult times The Vale could muster only one team or a part of one. Legend has it that a Vale worthy was once heard to exclaim in desperation, "If we don't get twelve next week I'm giving up!"

In a wooden changing hut, now long gone but still remembered with affection by The Vale ancients, the local authority, "The Corporation", as it used to be known in simpler times, had provided a stone bath fed by copper boilers heated from below by open gas rings. During the second half someone had to leave the field and nip off to the hut, which no-one bothered to lock, to light the gas. It provided an ideal opportunity for a quick gasper.

Since The Prairie belonged to the Corporation, during the summer it was available for other purposes: when the circus came to town that was where it went. It was the proudest boast of one of the mere mortals of rugby, whose exploits these tales record, that once, in the first match of the season, flying down the wing and about to score he was caught by a tap-tackle and fell headlong into a pile of lion dung. Few would claim this compares with winning The World Cup or even completing a Grand Slam but he became the first British player ever to be able to claim such a distinction on home soil. Had I been able to obtain a copy of the photograph which records that moment of triumph the reader would see it reproduced here, regardless of the expense, for even in many thousands of words I fear I would be unable to convey to the reader the spirit of rugby which that photograph encapsulates – the simple joy of taking part, the pleasure taken in achievements both great and small, whether our own or those of others, the unselfish camaraderie - but sadly we must place that photo amongst posterity's mounting losses. Yet, I trust, the reader will be able to imagine the scene: the man of the moment stands grinning, covered in glory, in the forefront of the picture, whilst in the background you can just make out his smiling team-mates; selflessly, they stand at a respectful distance, not wishing to encroach upon his personal triumph; in fact, any thought of mobbing the happy hero to steal some of his limelight could not be further from their minds.

They, that is the man of that particular moment, the supporting cast and the many more thousands like them, past and present, make up the mere mortals of rugby of whom I was one of the merest. These are our tales.

Not everyone can have the physical and other attributes necessary to play rugby at international level, at county level or even at first team level for their local club. But most people are lucky enough to be able to enjoy playing at some level. They are the ones who make up the vast majority of the rugby fraternity (or should I say "family" in these PC days?) They are otherwise known as "the grass roots". That's not a term I find inspirational. I prefer to call them the mere mortals. Without them there would be no immortals.

The mere mortals enjoy the freedom to play for no-one's entertainment but their own and that of their team-mates. I am not saying winning or losing does not matter to them for it certainly did to me. I would never have bothered turning out at all if I had not been playing to win and I do not know of anyone, even before the advent of leagues, who did not share that attitude. The winning or the losing of a match provided the context for that day and the week ahead. The accumulation of wins and losses provided the context for the season but we were fortunate to have the luxury that the results were not the be-all and end-all. Some years, amidst euphoria, records were broken for the number of games won and in other years they were broken, more quietly, for games lost. It all mattered hugely at the time but with the passage of the years the importance of those black and white statistics fades as the pages on which they are written yellow. Those simple records will always remain dumb as to the greater part of the story but as plain statistics they will probably last for ever in some shape or form. However, the collective memories of shared joys and woes, the wit and camaraderie which accompanied them both on and off the field have a built-in expiry date which the grim reaper ruthlessly enforces. So I have taken the responsibility – somebody had to – for putting some of the mere mortals' tales down on paper.

To some they will seem like small beer; I am sure there are funnier stories out there and I am certain there are much bigger ones. But these tales are the ones I know and, most importantly, they are the ones I can vouch for one hundred per cent. There was a storyteller at The Vale many years ago, and many a good yarn did he spin. His motto was never to let the truth stand in the way of a good story. I can easily understand why he thought this aberration was a virtue: a little embroidery here, a little deviation there seemed to "improve" the entertainment; the end justified the means. I will have none of that; I will not be tempted to follow my friend's example for I fear where it might lead. The road to hell is paved with good intentions; to keep the flow of play you start by ignoring the crooked feed at the scrum and before you know it you end up playing rugby league.

I must warn you that this book has been rejected by publishers on the grounds that, in the first place, demand would be likely to be limited to those of mature years who might be interested in the game of rugby at its less glamorous levels and they were thought to be few.

20

The additional requirement of literacy was expected to reduce the number of potential readers still further. Consequently, I have been obliged to self-publish. Nevertheless, I have taken account of certain criticisms made by acquaintances who know about these things. In order to accommodate the attention span of the average reader this book comes in self-contained chapters. The reader will be relieved to hear there is no need to follow a plot, let alone a sub-plot or even to remember what happened in the last chapter. Moreover, the chapters themselves are mostly quite short so that the reader will be able to complete at least one a week without straining his mental capacity. Though I say it myself, this book is refreshingly different from the "best-seller" or "page-turner" as it is eminently suited to being put down at any time and picked up again later whenever free time is available; there is no danger of the plot being lost or the reader's attention being so gripped that other activities in the daily round become neglected. Even so, just in case the stamina is not what it used to be I have arranged for a natural break when the oranges come on at half-time or for a breather to be taken when a player goes down injured. I have done my best to avoid the use of excessively flowery language but when it has been essential to add a little colour I have managed by recycling well-worn clichés. This has not only given me a warm feeling, knowing that my carbon footprint has not been increased by the use of the energy new imagery would have required, but also, as these figures of speech are already well known, the reader will waste no time pondering their meaning. Following the same reasoning, I have followed the usual player stereotypes the reader will be familiar with so that, unless otherwise stated a prop may be assumed to be both slow-moving and slow-witted, a wing forward sly and dirty, a three-quarter vain and effeminate etc.

Being by nature optimistic, I have supplied footnotes to assist the younger reader should there be one. These have been made necessary by the multiple changes which have been made in the laws of the game since the author was first privileged to step on to the field of play and which have been matched in at least equal measure by changes in the way the game of life is played.

I must hurry up now as the referee has left his changing room in his clean white shorts and his polished black boots with white laces and is on his way up to the pitch. I should just have time to give you a bit more background before the kick-off.

The location of The Vale itself is not important; you already know as much as is necessary. Had it been located elsewhere the details might have been different but the stories would have been similar. The most important thing is that The Vale was (is and always will be) the best rugby club ever in its own unique way, just as all other rugby clubs are the best in their own way. Maybe The Vale did not always have the best facilities. (As you know already the state of the pitches would have benefitted from some improvement). Perhaps I may have been in better clubhouses from time to time although I can't remember where. The players, as befitted the best club were also the best but when I say they were the best I am not saying they always played the best rugby because as I have already mentioned not everyone, no matter how hard they may try, can do that all the time. But, all things considered, they were and will continue to be the best. I am confident you will know what I mean but if my description should have conjured up an image of your own club rather than that of The Vale do not let it worry you; perhaps that's the way it should be.

Also, do not forget that as the reader you are the boss, so if you know Pablo, Wilf, Gordon or any of the others by a different name you are entirely at liberty to substitute them.

We must end the warm-up now as the referee is standing on the half-way line, beginning to look a bit agitated. He's got his whistle in his mouth and can't wait to start blowing it. As soon as the front row forwards get here we'll be able to start; they are on their way but they are walking up to the pitch so as to start the game in good condition.

Over the Wall

The evening my small part in these tales began found me as peeved as a wasp trapped in a jar; I was irritated with everything round me. My schooldays had lately passed, suddenly, into history. After sitting my last exam I had walked out of the building where I had been a pupil for the last seven years and caught the bus home. And that was it. Behind me the curtain fell silently. It cut me off from the daily reassurance of a long-running routine and signalled the beginning of the slow march to memory's frontiers of the supporting cast of hundreds of more or less familiar faces. Left standing alone, front of stage, as I waited for a new audience to fill the empty seats in the void before me it would have been easy to have allowed reflections on the past or speculations on the future to fill my mind. I could just as easily have been tempted to pursue mental images of crossroads, staging-posts, watersheds, rolling streams and the like. But I resisted manfully; no such thoughts penetrated my consciousness as I mooched about in the garden of the family home that evening. Deprived of the usual incentive of putting off homework, I could not find anything worth wasting my time on. In the vacuum boredom had crept up on me, found a willing mate in a sense of anti-climax and bred a nagging grievance which kept on telling me that I had been cheated out of something that those seven years at school had undoubtedly entitled me to: there should have been a piss-up after the exams.

We had all agreed before the exams started that there would be one. It had been a sustaining thought; something to look forward to; some compensation for the heavy slog. But now it was clear that we had cocked it up. Despite the enthusiasm with which the idea had been greeted no definite time or place had been set for it. Belatedly, I had begun to realise how important such seemingly minor details could be. Being novices at school leaving, we had failed to realise we would not be in daily contact any more once the exams started. Nobody had chosen the same combination of subjects as me so I had hardly seen any of my pals for weeks. Most had finished their exams before me. Some had already slipped away on holiday or had gone to take up vacation jobs. We were dispersing like tadpoles newly turned into frogs. By that evening I knew for certain the moment had been lost and that there wasn't going to be any celebration. It had all fizzled out like an expensive firework kept too long in the box. It just wasn't fair. Even the weather was making itself a source of irritation; it was one of those rare evenings in June when the sun, reluctant to take its leave, lays a glowing haze in which insects laze or jive as the mood takes them and the air is as light and comfortable as a cashmere sweater. Thunder and lightning would have suited my mood better.

The younger reader will be asking why I hadn't just rung round on my mobile to fix up the time and place. That is easily explained: I joined in these tales in the same year that Hancock scored his famous try at Twickenham for England against Scotland[2]. That was Andy Hancock, of course, not to be confused with Tony Hancock who at that time was famous for his "Half Hour". It was another twenty years later, before another famous comedian, Ernie Wise, made the first call on a commercial mobile phone network. He made that call to Vodafone's head office (which, incidentally, at that time was over a curry house in Newbury). The making of the call was actually televised in January 1985. It was, I think, basically intended as a send-up of one of those crazy ideas which will never catch on. The original piece of apparatus was known as the "talking brick"; it was the size of a briefcase and weighed eleven pounds[3], cost £2,000 then – which would have been approximately 2,250 pints in real money - and had a battery life of twenty minutes. Ninety per cent of under16s in this country now have a mobile phone. (The other ten per cent have recently lost theirs). Back in 1965 when Hancock scored his

---

[2] *Seen on the television in black and white. The first colour transmission of a sporting event was Wimbledon in 1967.*
[3] *That was before we went metric: eleven pounds would be five kilograms.*

try our household possessed a phone from the Bakelite[4] Age. It was a black and heavy two-piece instrument which was attached to a little box on the hall windowsill with a length of plaited, brown cord more commonly used for mooring barges on the canal. If you were fortunate enough to have a phone in your house that was the type of phone you had. It was the property of the G.P.O[5] and you rented it off them. The choice of phone was you either had one or you didn't and nobody thought anything more about it. Everybody could remember their number; ours was 833. We were lucky enough to have the phone because of my father's employment. It was a serious piece of equipment and the privilege of having it was not to be abused. I was frequently reminded that calls cost money to make; I was not expected to use the phone without both good reason and permission. Arranging a piss-up would not have qualified; I didn't need to bother asking. A typical conversation might have run as follows:-

Father: "Was that you on the phone just then? I didn't hear it ring."
Son: "It started to ring just as I was passing so I picked it up."
Father: "Who was it?"
Son: "Olly."
Father: "How convenient!"

Two such coincidences would not be expected to occur in the same evening. There was no getting away from it; it was a monumental, irretrievable cock-up. And, much as I tried, I couldn't get away from it; my mind kept returning to it like an unsolved problem.

To make matters worse, now that I had left school, for some reason all the older generation kept banging on about oysters and how the world had suddenly become one big one. I had never eaten even a small one and I didn't quite know what they meant but I wasn't going to show my ignorance by asking. I got the impression it was supposed

---

[4] *The trade name of an early plastic which was hard but brittle.*
[5] *The G.P.O was the General Post Office officially established in 1660 by Charles II. It became The Post Office in 1969. It had the monopoly of postal and telephone services at the time.*

to be something good coming my way - in the future, of course, - but these were the same people who, up till recently, had been telling me, with more repeats than BBC2, that my schooldays would be the best years of my life. What a load of bull that was; such an obvious insult to the intelligence it was not even worth a teenager's derisory snort. However, no sooner were my schooldays over than they had changed the record. Typical but annoying none the less; just another ingredient to stir into the festering mix of frustration and irritation.

As these thoughts buzzed round impotently inside my head the sound of voices and laughter began to drift over from the rugby ground a hundred yards or so across the field next to our house. Although it had been there couple of years it had remained unexplored territory to me. I had known it well in its former identity as old farmer Dinsdale's hay meadow; I had been chased out of there many a time. But since they had fenced the old meadow off properly and erected those tall, slightly crooked, intimidating goalposts I had kept out. Funny game that; must be funny people who played it. I had watched it on television when there was nothing else on. Why would anyone want to play a game like that? It was completely alien to an enthusiastic young soccer player: the ball didn't bounce properly for a start; sometimes it was just hoofed up the field and everybody ran after it like a load of junior school kids. Where was the skill in that? When they did pass the ball they passed it backwards although the purpose of the game was obviously to go forwards. There were various melées where you couldn't see what was going on and the referee kept blowing his whistle for no apparent reason. Then, instead of pointing in the direction the side awarded the free kick were playing, he turned the opposite way and did what looked suspiciously like a Nazi salute. Very odd and a bit sinister really. To add to the puzzle there were two different versions of the game; one lot played for money but the other lot were amateurs. That was fair enough but why two different sets of rules? After all there were professional and amateur soccer teams but they managed to get by on just one set of rules; what did rugby need two lots for? It was a minority sport to start with; why split the vote and make it worse? It was never going to catch up with soccer; there was no way it could ever compete.

Eddie Waring commented on the professional game with an exaggerated northern accent which grated on me. "That's two fo' Wig-ern", was one of his trademark sayings. We adopted it in our schoolyard games of soccer. If someone skied a shot spectacularly over the bar. "Two," we would shout and after a slight pause, "for Wigan!" We were not just mocking the player who had made the shot but deriding the game of rugby itself which was not so much incomprehensible to us as inconceivable.

Overall rugby league was presented on the television as rather, what we would now call, "down-market". In a reversal of the situation in soccer it was the amateur game which seemed to have the glamour, if that could be the right word when all the players, whether amateur or professional, seemed to be covered in mud after the first ten minutes. A Scottish bloke commented on the amateur game; his accent at least sounded genuine. He communicated a passion and sincerity for the game and it might have made more sense if I had been able to understand half of what he was talking about. The amateur teams seemed to be populated with names like Reginald Farquar-Smythe and Nigel Ponsonby-Holmes. Obviously, they were posh. Oddly, a chap called Gary Owen always seemed to put in a brief appearance no matter which team was playing. Another interesting thing was that there was no goalkeeper. Instead both sides had to play with a fool back; it seemed a quirky sort of handicap but I supposed it was fair to both sides. "He's through! He's only got the fool back to beat!" No problem there then. The fool back had a number 15 on his shirt unless he was playing for Bath or Richmond in which case it was 16 so that they did not have an unlucky 13 on the pitch. At first sight it looked like Leicester had given him a zero but when you saw their other players it was clear that they had decided that mere numbers were not good enough for them and it was actually the letter 'O'. Bristol had gone for letters as well but, not wanting to be thought of as on the same level as Leicester, they had started their system the other way round so that their full back had the letter 'A' on

27

his back. Meanwhile the professionals had him as number 1 but they only played with thirteen men anyway. I supposed it helped to keep the wages bill down. It was all completely barmy. No thank you. I would stick to football. And that was yet another daft thing about rugby: they called that football as well but it was obvious you were supposed to play the game with your hands; clearly it should have been called rugby handball. More nonsense.

But there were some things I did like about rugby; professional soccer players had recently taken to writhing on the floor in agony after the slightest contact. Two minutes later they would be haring down the wing and you would never have guessed both their legs were broken. And all the hugging and kissing after a goal was scored. Yuck! It was only a game, after all, but it was supposed to be a man's game. I probably would not have recognised the word or the cause at that tender age but a certain boorishness was entering the game following the abolition of the maximum wage[6]. There was none of that sort of behaviour in rugby. Players got flattened, got up and got on with it without even bothering to dust themselves down or scrape the mud off. If somebody stayed down you knew he really was hurt.

It was also clear that, whatever strange signals the referee might make, his word was law; there was no arguing; you didn't appeal to the referee; you didn't talk back to the referee; in fact, you didn't talk to the referee at all. Otherwise he would just blow his whistle and award a penalty or, if he had already awarded one he would march ten yards up the pitch and re-award the penalty from there. No messing: much better.

Another thing was that when a player scored a try he just carried the ball back and put it down where the resulting kick at goal was to be taken. In a really exceptional case he might very quickly, almost apologetically, shake the hand of the player who had given him the scoring pass but, usually, no acknowledgement of any kind was

---

[6] *The maximum wage professional soccer clubs were allowed to pay was abolished in 1961.*

considered necessary. It all seemed more manly and more about the team than the individual. Still completely barmy, nevertheless.

Those menacing goal posts had been taken down now for the summer; the playing season had ended several weeks ago in an earlier lifetime before the exams had started. Once again there was just an open expanse of grass; it looked like old farmer Dinsdale's meadow after hay-time once more. The voices I had heard belonged to more than a dozen men in shorts. They were kicking a football about, a proper round one. It looked like just an informal game: a kick-about. They were all wearing different shirts and the goals were just piles of tops; it was a scene I was familiar with from the local recs[7] which I had often visited in search of a game. I suddenly wondered if I could get one now. Why not? I wasn't a schoolboy any longer. It was worth a try; anything to get away from this itching irritation. The stairs to my bedroom were taken two at a time. Moments later I was changed, down the garden and over the wall.

There were two fences to get over and a field to cross. Somewhere along the way it occurred to me that I was going to look very silly and small if I had to come all the way back again with my tail between my legs. But it was too late now. I arrived at the side of the pitch trying not to betray my apprehension: they might say I wasn't a member so piss off. After all it was private property, not like the rec. I might even get told off for climbing over the fence. But so far so good; I got to the side of the makeshift pitch without being shouted at. There I followed the protocol I had learnt at the recs, even though, I worried myself by thinking, as they were rugby players they probably had some totally different, back to front way of doing things which only they understood. I waited near the halfway line on the edge of the playing area, which was still marked out by a fading whitewash burn, without making eye contact with anyone. According to the protocol there was an appropriate period during which you were expected to assess whether you could match the standard of play

---

[7] *Recreation grounds maintained by local councils*

before asking if you could join in. From what I saw I was sure I could. When the ball went out of play near me I took my opportunity; I fetched it, caught the eye of the person who looked like he had the authority and asked boldly in the time-honoured phrase, "Can I have a game?"

Without hesitation the person I had asked, a short, stocky guy with a low centre of gravity, gave me the nod and motioned which end to play towards. He was pretty old; I reckoned he must be at least thirty. He had a sudden, twinkling smile and the advanced stages of a Bobby Charlton haircut.[8] That was where any resemblance he or any of the others had to being a footballer in the soccer sense ended. I was no twinkle-toes myself. I had been blessed with feet which were embarrassingly large when I was small. Since then I had grown into them a bit so that messages from the brain did not seem to take just as long to reach their destination. My role on the soccer pitch was that of a stopper. When I was successful in that capacity I would swing the mighty right boot and hoof the ball in the general direction of a team mate downfield. Imagine my delight when I discovered I was able to dribble at will from one end of the pitch to the other before crowning my efforts by striking it or stroking it past the wooden, stand-in keeper, every time; no problem, no mercy. Though I was obviously right-footed, and only right-footed, they always bought that little shimmy to the left. Pure joy. Sometimes for a change I would, unselfishly, lay on the scoring pass.

We played for an hour or so and I could have done at least another two without the slightest chance of getting bored or tired. But all good things must come to an end and they did when the short,

---

[8]*Now Sir Bobby Charlton, a member of the England soccer team which won the World Cup in 1966. He endeavoured to disguise the fact he was going a bit thin on top by training long strands of his remaining hair over his dome. The style came to be known as the "comb-over", was copied by many as baldness then was definitely not considered sexy but, eventually, it was cruelly put to death by parody in a series of "Hamlet" cigar adverts.*

stocky guy declared enough. I was about to make my way back home in a much better mood when he said, "Why don't you come down to the clubhouse for a pint?" My jaw slackened. A what? I knew they must have changing rooms down at the clubhouse but the possibility that they might also have a bar had not occurred to me – how truly, incredibly strange that now seems with hindsight! Had I not found it necessary to explain I had no money on me I would have been speechless.

"Don't worry about that. I'll buy you one," said my new hero. Well, my mother had always told me not to accept sweets off strangers but she never said anything about pints. Now I really was speechless. Whilst concentrating hard on not getting too far in front of everyone else in the walk down to the clubhouse I still managed to congratulate myself as it seemed quite likely I had single-handedly discovered an entirely new, much more advanced form of civilisation, virtually on my own doorstep. Perhaps there was going to be something in this oyster business after all.

The stocky guy with the twinkling smile turned out to be the captain of the rugby club. As I gazed round, taking in the interior of the clubhouse and especially the handpumps on the bar, he asked "What would you like a pint of? Youngers or McEwans?" I almost had to pinch myself. Beer usually meant the local brew although it wouldn't have mattered to me what it was. I had been fortunate to sample a pint or two of Youngers in the Dales where landlords seemed a bit more liberal in their interpretation of the legal age requirements[9] but the word was that McEwans was even better. The only problem was that it was nearly impossible to find. Yet here it was: ale's Holy Grail, on tap, on the bar right in front of me not half a mile from where I lived. It was unbelievable. For the next few moments I might have stood there with my mouth open like a little lad first time in a sweet shop had I not been busy gulping down beer.

---

[9] *At that time it was an offence either to consume alcohol on licensed premises if under 18 or to purchase alcohol for consumption by someone under that age.*

The captain introduced me to some of the other rugby players who had taken part in the kick-about. They not only seemed very friendly but surprisingly normal and they bought me another pint before they went off to get changed. That seemed my cue to leave but before I did so I asked, "Will you be playing next week?" They were and I was over the wall again as soon as the first figures and a ball appeared. I had brought some money with me this time. However, although I offered I was not allowed to buy, not because I was under age or was not a member but because I was a student. Although that status was still dependent on exam results I didn't complain. This time I was shown round the changing facilities. There were some decent looking showers and a large hot water tank but the most impressive feature was a huge bath. I had never seen anything like it. At school we had showers which were not brilliant but, as I had discovered, a lot better than nothing. That was the usual situation in the local amateur soccer league where I had played on Saturday afternoons over the last couple of seasons. The changing rooms we had at our home ground were just that; somewhere to change under cover. There was no electricity, no running water and, of course, no heating. In the depths of winter, if you did not get a move on you could find yourself finishing getting changed in near darkness before walking to the bus stop to wait for the bus home. If you had been able to keep your socks up all afternoon, with luck, only your knees and thighs would be covered in mud. If you got the worst off once you got your trousers on your body heat would gradually dry the rest off especially if you were fortunate enough to get one of the new buses which were just coming into service and actually had heaters. We all knew which seats they were under. If you could get the warm air to circulate up your trouser legs the mud would start to flake off. I had two buses to catch to get home after a game so sometimes I could be quite clean by the time I got there.

Some weeks I also played soccer for the school on Saturday mornings. It did not take me long to work out that there was not much point having a shower, which was often cold anyway, after the school game to get muddy again in the afternoon on the other side of a

32

packed lunch. I got quite used to spending most of Saturday caked in mud. More than once, arriving home after the second game I was distracted by something interesting on television and went out again without having a bath. Mother would have been horrified had she known my dark secret.

My hosts assured me there was always plenty of hot water to fill the big bath; it hadn't been filled that evening because there weren't enough people to justify it but the showers were good anyway. It was suggested that if I wanted, member or not, next week I could get changed there and join in fully instead of having to go home after a couple of pints. The invitation was accepted without hesitation.

It was my third week now and I was beginning to feel part of the scene, pint pot[10] in hand at the bar; not quite a man amongst men as I was still in awe of some of the rugby players. A few were well over six feet tall and well built and some of the shorter ones stood square like the proverbial external closet. They all appeared as if they could look after themselves.

I knew a few of them well enough to talk to by now and the conversation, inevitably, turned to sport in general and rugby in particular. Had I ever played? Why not? I would enjoy it. If you could catch a ball and run rugby was the game, especially if you liked a pint or two afterwards. And nobody ever got injured. Well, not seriously anyway. You might expect to pick up a few knocks and bruises but in terms of serious injury soccer was the more dangerous game. Far more dangerous. People broke legs playing soccer and were out of the game for the season, if not longer. Then when people went to head the ball there could be clashes of heads. Dreadful. In fact, just heading a heavy ball could lead to brain damage. There was none of that in rugby. I was shocked; I had been playing soccer all those years and

---

[10] *At that time pint glasses in the North were almost exclusively of the "dimple" or "barrel" type, heavy, sturdy and with a handle: considered altogether more masculine than the sleeves or schooners favoured down South.*

had never realised what a dangerous game it was. The thing about soccer was, they said, that you could go a long time without getting any injuries at all but when you did get one it was likely to be serious whereas with rugby you probably got a bit of a bruise or something every week. When you added everything up you probably got hurt as much playing rugby as you did soccer, perhaps even a bit more, but it all came in easy instalments.

"Young, fit lad like you. He won't have any problem at all, will he?" asked the skipper and the fellow conspirators all shook their heads reassuringly.

Not wanting to say that I didn't relish the idea of getting flattened even if it didn't hurt as much as it looked like it did, I tried to explain that I had missed the end of the soccer season due to a knee injury and ...

"Well, that's just the trouble with soccer, hard on the joints, especially the knees. But, in rugby, you see, you tend to take all the knocks on the upper body."

Others nodded and confirmed that rugby was not hard on the knees at all. In fact, you hardly needed knees at all to play rugby. The good news just kept coming.

Training started the third Saturday in July. I was there. All shapes and sizes turned up. I was amazed how old some of them looked. And how unfit they were. There was puffing and panting and grunting and groaning on a scale that would not have disgraced a gym full of geriatrics. Red-faced distress was common and there were even people being sick on the sidelines. There would be three training sessions a week from then on: Monday and Wednesday evenings as well as Saturday afternoon. However, I noticed that those players who seemed most in need of some physical fitness training were only to be seen on a Saturday, if at all.

It was decided early on that I should be a "three" because I "could run a bit". That sounded fair enough to me; I knew there fifteen in a team and to be just one of three sounded like I was joining a select group. I was soon disabused of that notion by one of the retired players who had come along to assist with training. He had been assigned the task of giving clueless converts such as myself some rudimentary notion of what we were supposed to do. In my case that was going to be to stand on the wing with a simple mission: if the ball came to me I was to catch it, run like hell to the other end and touch it down beyond the line the posts were standing on but before the second line. If the ball came to the bloke opposite me I had to stop him, scrag him, get the ball off him and run like hell etc. That was all I needed to know to start with. There didn't seem much to it.

At the next session, after the basic fitness training we were told to divide up into forwards and backs. So, naturally, now that I knew I was going to be on the wing I joined the forwards. We did some strange exercises which didn't seem to have a lot to do with running like hell etc. but who was I to know? Then we were told we were going to do some scrummaging practice and I thought to myself that it did not really correspond with the image I had in my head of me flying down the wing with the wind blowing through my lengthening mane[11] but, I supposed there must be some advantage in knowing about these things if I was going to play the game; it was a training session after all. A big guy came over and asked me where I "packed down" and I thought, "Here we go; we're back to the nonsense again." Before I could say anything he suggested "Wing forward?" and I thought, "That's it! - forward - on the wing – wing-forward; there was a bit of logic to it after all". "Take the open side," he said. Just as I was thinking, "Here's the nonsense back again," there was suddenly a lot of grunting and I noticed I was the only one left standing up. The big guy shouted at me impatiently to get packed down and I realised that some immediate action was required on my part; obviously, "the open side" obviously did not mean stay in the open: I was meant to

---

[11] *Short back and sides was the order of the day. If cleanliness was next to godliness short hair came a close second. I had been rebelling, with limited success, against both parental and school diktat for some time and if I ever got to university I was not going to have my hair cut again, ever.*

join in with the rest of them. But where? The timing did not seem just right to be seeking guidance about the niceties of "packing down" and, in any event, I was at an age where not already knowing everything was definitely not cool. I'd seen them pushing and shoving on television so I launched myself into what appeared to be the gap left for me with the mightiest shove I could muster. Almost immediately I found myself sprawled across several bodies amidst a whole lot of cursing and swearing. I was the first to my feet but was very quickly joined by the big guy. He was rubbing his neck and seemed a bit annoyed as he looked down on me. He had a smear of mud down the side of his face and some blades of grass decorating his left eyebrow. He did look rather comical. However, it seemed appropriate to leave it to someone with whom he was better acquainted to tell him about it; I thought it better for me not to mention it just at that moment because his general demeanour was completely changed from the mild-mannered bloke I had been chatting to after the kick-about a couple of weeks back. Somehow he looked even bigger without his jacket on and, in fact, I've got to say he seemed a bit fierce. For some reason he appeared to think I was responsible for his present discomfort because he asked me, not too politely, what the fuck I had done that for. Despite the tenderness of my years I recognised the situation I was in: one has inadvertently caused someone a serious problem by one's conduct and some kind of cogent explanation is urgently required but one has not a clue where to start. It was definitely one of those "What? When? Who? Me?" moments. Just then someone else I recognised intervened. He was rubbing his neck as well and also seemed to be on the grumpy side of when I had last enjoyed his company.

"You're supposed to be in the backs," he said. "They're over there."

He didn't need to add any further encouragement as I was already on my way in the direction pointed. As I trotted away like a chastised puppy I succumbed to the thought that this rugby game might not be just as simple as they had made out.

Yippee aye ay

Yippee aye ay
Yippee aye ...o... o... o ... o ... o ...
.... Ghost riders in the sky... aye... aye

This was always a popular song at The Vale. As it had a chorus it allowed for some extemporisation by those who thought they had the vocal range (of whom there were many after a few pints) whilst those who were more modest in their singing ability could at least join in heartily. Unusually, there were one or two amongst the players who actually knew the words to all the verses so that the singing did not share the fate of the guttering candle as often happened with the less well-known ditties. Consequently, it was normally well worth the effort to suspend any conversation and join in. In a good performance the chorus would echo from one side of the clubhouse to the other often aided by the intervention of a self-appointed conductor who would determine when the chorus should end and the next verse begin. It wasn't really a "rugby song" because it contained no obscenities and I presumed that was the reason it was not in the book I had bought. Following my difficulties at training I had been to the bookshop in search of some reading material[12]. All I had been able to find was a book about rugby songs but I bought it anyway; it seemed a good idea to widen my general knowledge of the game if I was going to associate myself with this rugby lot. When I got home I found out they had missed out all the naughty words. I managed to work most of them out but I struggled with some, in particular:-

***** ***** no ***** at all

---

[12] *In those days, before the internet existed, if you wanted to find something out for yourself you had either to borrow a book from the library or buy one.*

37

And

Roll tiddly oh **** or bust
Never let your eight asterisks dangle in the dust.

Whilst I may have been better prepared to join in the singing I was no wiser regarding the actual playing of the game when I turned up for the next training session. There were some new faces, well new to me, and as the weeks progressed more and more came along, swelling the total to fifty or sixty or so. Some had been away on their annual holidays; others had delayed their arrival at the training sessions as they did not want to wear themselves out before the season began. There were so many that I began to wonder whether I would get a game when the season did start. I could see I was fitter than the majority but they would obviously have more idea about actually playing. My main asset was that I was reasonably quick. That much had been observed at the informal soccer kick-abouts which had got me involved in the first place but put a rugby ball in my hands with a couple of great hairy behemoths chasing me and it was noted that I went even faster. They gave up after a few yards but I didn't know that; I wasn't going to waste any time looking behind me. But I did get caught in one training session and my shirt, an old soccer shirt which had a white polo-neck collar got ripped off me just leaving just the collar so that I spent the rest of the game running about like an unfrocked vicar. After that session I was taken aside by one of the older players and told that once I had been tackled to the ground I had to release the ball otherwise I might get rucked. I was less worried after he confirmed that I had heard him correctly. He explained that "rucking" was rugby-speak for the application of the boot. It was very handy to be made aware of the odd rule from time to time.

I was surprised at the percentage who appeared to be over thirty, well over in some cases. In the local amateur soccer league very few seemed to carry on beyond that milestone. Another thing that was different to soccer was the range of shapes and sizes. Generally speaking, whilst you did very occasionally get particularly tall soccer players or, more often, particularly short ones, height did not normally vary all that much. Similarly regarding build, again with some

38

exceptions, the norm was for the soccer player to be built on reasonably athletic lines. Not so with these rugby players; athleticism was not a word which sprang to mind: they came in all shapes and sizes and there were not many who looked under-nourished. There were some very tall blokes which fitted in with my general perception of a rugby player but there were others who were quite short which was a surprise to me. Even more of a surprise was that some of the short blokes didn't have any weight about them either. Anyway, I was pleased to note that they were not all beefed up sado-masochists – far from it – and there was a greater cross section of physique represented than there would have been in an equivalent gathering of soccer players. True, there was a general tendency towards the stronger and heavier build but there were more exceptions than rules. It wasn't what I had expected but I liked it; it seemed, strangely and unexpectedly, more egalitarian than soccer which, basically, is a game you are physically cut out for or you are not. Paradoxically, despite its image, rugby was more open; anyone could play as they would find a position which suited their physique. I found this inclusiveness refreshing. Essentially, if you could not run or if you could not see you could not play soccer. Yet here were blokes who could do neither, happily playing rugby. These blokes played in the forwards, usually in the front row. The Vale had at least one pair of complementary front row forwards when I joined. They were both about 5'7" and generously built. I was told that one was a loose head and the other a tight head. Although I observed them as carefully as I could without wishing to appear rude, I couldn't see any difference. I would not say they were optically challenged but despite having thick, strong necks, their heads tended to dip forward slightly when they put their glasses on. Once they had them on, one of them made you think Big Brother [13]was watching you as these great big eyes seemed to follow you wherever you might try to hide but with the other one all you could see behind his glasses were two little dots like when the telly had just

---

[13] *A reference to "1984" by George Orwell which created the idea; not the TV programme.*

been turned off. Once on the field they looked like a pair of huge moles in hooped shirts. Of course, they could not wear their glasses on the field[14] but they did not need them in the front row of the tight scrum. When the scrum was over, being naturally the last up, they just used to amble off together behind the other forwards in the general direction of play, not quite holding hands as that kind of thing would have been frowned on in those days[15], but keeping very close together so as not to get lost. It was quite touching to watch. On arriving at the breakdown one of them would instinctively burrow into a gap which a sighted person would never have noticed and shortly afterwards the ball would appear presented by a pair of hands like steam shovels which did not appear to belong to anyone in particular. They say that when one of the senses is impaired the others improve to help to make up the deficit and it was rumoured they were able to smell the leather of the ball.

Because they were normally somewhat behind open play they did not usually have to worry about seeing the ball if it was passed to them but on the few occasions that happened they dropped it as a matter of course. All forwards were expected at that time to do that anyway. The referee would then blow for a knock-on and they could have another scrummage. That was all the forwards, and front row forwards in particular wanted to do: scrummage.

I was already becoming sceptical about the claim that you did not need knees to play rugby but I did see some visible justification for it at one session. There was a bloke whose legs were so short he didn't have room for any knees; his shorts came right down to his stocking tops. He turned out to be a scrum-half. I found out that, for some reason, scrum-halves tended to be short. They also tended to be quite stocky, relatively speaking. When Floyd Patterson regained the undisputed world heavyweight boxing championship from Ingemar

---

[14] *It was not until the late 70s that the manufacture of contact lenses improved to the extent that they became an option for most people.*
[15] *Until The Sexual Offences Act of 1967 all types of homosexual act were illegal although this possibly did not include hand-holding.*

Johanson in 1960 he was 6 feet tall and weighed all of thirteen stone. He lost the title again to the monster, Sonny Liston who was half an inch taller and all of 15 stone. Mike Phillips the Welsh international and Lions scrum half is 6′3″ tall and weighs over 16 stone. Nowadays, when you see the players lining up before international matches you think some of them don't look all that big but then you realise they are standing between a couple of blokes at 6'7" each weighing in at nineteen or more stone. The French three-quarters who lined up against Scotland in February 2010 had an average weight of sixteen stone, the shortest being Bastereaud at 6′0′. We had a scrum-half who certainly could not be described as tall or stocky. I am not saying he was short as he would have had no trouble whatsoever eyeballing Mike Phillips' belly button but I bet his weight doubled in the course of a game on a wet day. He used to disappear into the mud with both packs of forwards on top of him and I would be thinking to myself that that would be the last we would ever see of him when all of a sudden he would pop out, completely unscathed apart from being even muddier, start shouting at the pack and really chucking his weight around. He was Welsh, of course. Every club had to have a Welsh scrum-half or if it didn't have one at the time, had just had one or was just about to get one. I suppose there must have been a lot of English scrum-halves playing in Wales to balance it up. I think the reason we got so many Welshmen at The Vale was that they felt at home in the valley with the green sward and the fast flowing river. Also there were the blue Welsh slates on the roofs of the terraces of stone-built houses which hugged the sides of the valley, not to mention the bardic broodiness of the surrounding hills with their flocks of good-looking sheep.

One of those little mysteries of life that I never managed to work out was that the scrum-half in question was not called Taffy.

However, what I, as a newcomer to the game, liked about scrum-halves and prop forwards was that they were just that: no complications. All right there was that business about tight-head and loose-head but as long as they knew which was which I wasn't going to let it bother me. And a scrum-half was a scrum-half and that was that; he wasn't called anything else. I supposed that at some posh club he might have had a number on his shirt and, consequently, be referred to as "the number nine" but there wasn't that problem at The Vale. Hooker was straightforward. Although we didn't have numbers (or letters) on our shirts full back was easy to work out from where he was standing. Conversely, the number eight was a bit more tricky. (I never bothered to worry about what they called him at Leicester and Bristol). But after that we were back to the usual nonsense: in the pack of eight there were the front row forwards: three of them, a couple of second row forwards, two flankers, some locks, three in the back row, a blindside, a hooker,some breakaways, an openside ... but, just a minute, that was well into double figures already. It didn't add up. The situation in the backs was only a little less confusing. The full back position seemed clear enough and I had learnt at the last session that a winger was also in the backs. There were two wingers, left and right which was logical enough. There were also two centres. In soccer they had a centre half and centre forward each of which played in the centre of the field, one in front of the other. Of course, such a set-up was far too simple for rugby; they had two "centre three-quarters". How was that possible? I mean someone is either in the centre or not in the centre and what happened to the other quarter? Where was that supposed to go? In the lower teams the centres tended to be left and right as it saved a lot of walking about but more often there was an "inside" centre and an "outside centre" although both centres played inside the wingers and outside the outside half. Two wingers and two centres made four three quarters. If that was a bit complicated it was nothing compared to the chap who partnered the scrum half. He varied between the outside half, the stand-off, the first receiver, the fly-half, the five eighths and the out-half and I dare say that if we had had numbers on the shirts they would probably have called him the number ten as well but as far as I could see it was the same bloke all the time. After one training session I thought I would get some help to sort all these confusing things out. I looked round the clubhouse for my sponsors, the blokes who had got me involved in the first place, but they were otherwise engaged so I got talking to a group of blokes who had just recently started turning up at training. I could see they were better at getting round the beer than they had been at getting round the training pitch but they were friendly and happy bunch. They soon managed to explain things to me. This was the gist of it:-

"What you've got in the scrum is, effectively, three rows of forwards. There are three in the front row, two in the second row and three in the back row."

"That makes eight all together."

"Correct."

"Well, I think I've got the front row worked out; that's the two props and the hooker. But where do the locks come in?"

"That's just another name for the two second rows. They lock the scrum and do all the pushing. That's why they call them the donkeys as well."

"Right. So Sam's a second row then? I wouldn't have thought he was big enough."

" No. He's called a donkey for a different reason. He plays wing forward."

"So 'donkey' is another name for a wing forward as well, then?"

"No. But wing forwards are also called flankers or break-aways. You've got one wing forward on one side of the scrum. He's the open-side wing forward with the Number 8 in the middle and the one on the other side is called the blind-side."

"Why is it called 'the blind-side'?"

"Because the referee can't see what's going on."

And that was it in a nutshell. All the confusion about the stand-off/fly-half etc. was as I had thought: it was the same bloke but they just had several different names for the same position. I didn't bother asking why as it didn't surprise me: the rugby lot couldn't keep anything straightforward.

Things were going well but into every life a little rain must fall: the McEwans Bitter ran out. It did not seem to worry the lads I was with.

"Try the Yippee Aye Ay, John," they said, "that's Younger's I.P.A. on draught. It's more or less the same as the McEwans – isn't it, lads?"

They all agreed it was and I would never have believed it but do you know what? It went down even better than the McEwans. As some Scottish chappie once remarked, "The minutes winged their way with pleasure". Somebody suggested we sat down and had a game of cards. That was a mistake. The sitting down, I mean, not the game of cards. We played for pints, some game I'd never played before. It must have been beginner's luck as I did seem to get plenty of beer; extremely generous those lads were: I hardly seemed to have got half way down one before somebody was buying me another. However, as the same Scottish chappie remarked later on in the script, "Nae man can tether time or tide" or even stop the bell ringing time for that matter and finally we had to go. Amidst much hand-shaking and back-slapping I took my leave of my new-found friends, went out into the bright, moonlit evening, took a deep breath of the cool, fresh air and realised I was horribly pissed. At first I thought I had been the victim of a practical joke and that somebody had tied a scarf round my legs as they didn't seem to want to move but, in fact, with a little help from my friends I had become another victim of the yippee aye ay. I was not the first and would not be the last. A while later I discovered that I had joined distinguished company; one of many other victims was another youthful Vale conscript who, years before, had been persuaded by the elders he supposed his betters that there was nothing to consuming four pints of the stuff between entering and leaving the bath at Chapelton Lunesdale and thus, very shortly afterwards, he earned the nickname of "Sicky". It marked the beginning of the end of his parents' fond aspirations for him that he should enter the Methodist Ministry; the fact he later came to be captain of The Vale was of no consolation to them.

So there I was alone in the moonlight. I was grateful home was not far away and that I still knew roughly where it was. It took me a fair while to stagger there. (I could have probably gone quicker if I could have got the scarf off my legs but I didn't dare to bend down to try to untie it). On the way it occurred to me that it was perhaps no bad thing if it took me a while as I was hoping my mother and father would be in bed asleep and I was pleased to note that the whole house was in darkness as I approached. I let myself in at the back door – never locked because there was only one key - and crept silently through the hall, only bumping into one chair and the coffee table; the other chair and the grandfather's clock had the decency not to take advantage of my condition and left me alone. I made it to the bottom of the stairs, still progressing as silently as would a small rodent. I began to ascend the stairs on all fours – purely to distribute the weight, you understand, in order to minimise the risk of the stairs creaking – and I was nearly at the top when, despite all my precautions one of the stairs did creak slightly. Not a loud creak though and I was confident I had got away with it when suddenly the entire place was brightly illuminated, revealing my closest paternal ancestor at the top of the stairs, looking very tall for his height and rather displeased as if someone had just woken him up. He asked me what I thought I was doing. It was difficult to ignore the obvious invitation to sarcasm yet I somehow managed to do so. I think there was something in the abrupt manner he put the question which made me think it might be more appropriate to offer a simple explanation rather than try the clever stuff. But even the simple words would not come and I found myself doing a passable imitation of a goldfish. It was perhaps a little late in the evening for my new-found talent for piscine mimicry to be entirely appreciated for words of criticism were followed by a further question of a similar nature to the first: "I suppose you think you're funny?" That may not be verbatim after all these years but it is fairly close. For my part, I suppose I should have realised that this was intended as one of those rhetorical questions to which no response was strictly necessary but the lateness of the hour combined with my rather awkward position on the stairs must have contributed to my failing to detect the subtlety of the intonation in my father's voice and I responded with an encore of the goldfish impression. Although I'm sure it was an improvement on my first attempt, when I looked up the dial on the fatherly barometer offered no change in the current icy conditions but foretold the probability of storms ahead. Clearly, my efforts had failed to awaken the spirit of merriment still slumbering deep in the paternal psyche. He made some pithy observations both on my current condition and my capabilities as a comedian then just as suddenly as it had become light it went dark again.

I hastened to complete my journey and crawled into bed. I was only just in time; had I got there any later it would have left without me. For no sooner had I got in than it set off round the room at a fair old lick, emulating a roller coaster every time it came to a corner. Now I've never been one for fairground rides and as soon as it slowed down a bit I had to jump off to go and be sick.

Fortunately, I did not spend the rest of the night lying awake wondering whether, before our next meeting, the funny side of our encounter might have crept up on my father as it would have been a complete waste of time. I believe that around that time he began to have doubts not just about me playing rugby but about me in general and he did not appreciate the funny side of that incident at all until many years later when I was at the other end to his grandson of a similar event which he thought was hilarious.

Carded

The Wednesday before the first Saturday in September I was surprised to receive a postcard through the post; it was from The Vale informing me I had been selected to play for them that week. Apart from that being good news in itself, receiving an actual card made me feel rather important. I had always been informed of my selection for the amateur league soccer team by word of mouth. The card said I had been selected to play for the 'B' XV. (Fortunately, I had done latin at school so I knew what they meant). But that was amazing: my first game for The Vale and I was to play in the second team. I thought they would have started me in the fourth team. When I went to the final training session that evening I found out I was in the fourth team. It turned out the First XV was the First XV- impeccable logic there - the second team was the 'A' XV, the third team the 'Extra A' and the fourth team was the 'B' XV. I was wondering once again whether these rugby players weren't a funny lot after all; they seemed to have a mental block when it came to doing anything in a straightforward way.

"Meet at the Clubhouse," the pre-printed card had said, "at 2.15pm." I arrived a quarter of an hour early to find that the entrance to the clubhouse was already piled high with kit bags. There were a few older members and retired players, some of whom had come to help with the organisation and others who had just come for a drink before watching the game. They were chatting, pints in hand, whilst various groups of players ostentatiously drank orange squash. The hum of conversation formed the background to occasional outbursts of laughter, and to the jeers, cheers and insults which greeted new arrivals. Befitting the prelude to the first match of the season the atmosphere was lightly charged with excitement. I knew who the fourth team captain was. I spotted him and went over to report.

"Not with us today," he said, "you've been promoted."

Well, that was dazzling news! Not a pass dropped nor a tackle missed and I was already on the up. Before I could adequately reflect

47

on my good fortune or even seek further details of it I was grabbed by
the shoulders by a much larger individual I'd seen in training, but not
had any dealings with, and hustled towards the door.

"Come on! Grab your kit; you're late!"

At first I could not see how I could possibly be late as kick-off
was not until 3pm. but as I being propelled towards the car park rather
than the changing rooms it began to occur to me that my first game for
The Vale was going to be away. This seemed strange as I had thought
that only the first XV was playing away that afternoon. However, my
attempt to raise the point was gruffly silenced and the need for haste
reiterated. I seemed to be getting the blame for us being late but I
decided to keep my sense of injustice to myself in view of the other's
seniority, not to mention the disparity in height and weight, his
demeanour and rather intimidating bent nose and cauliflower ear. He
was not a man of many words and it appeared anyway that he needed
all his powers of concentration for driving at a speed which failed by a
fair margin to conform to the legal limits. I only managed to glean that
we were on our way to another club not so far away. During training I
had come across some seriously large and hard looking guys to whom
I had mentally awarded first team status. Even during training games
they had not seemed to care much about where they put their feet or
for life and limb in general. Added to the fact that I had only slightly
more of a clue as to what I was supposed to be doing than when I
started there was a scary aspect to my sudden elevation to stardom.

The twinkle was absent from the skipper's eye when he
greeted our arrival at the opposition's clubhouse with the information
that we were late. My captor's excuse that he had had to wait for me
received short shrift:

"He's not even supposed to be here anyway, you great
pudding! He should be playing at home. I don't know where you got
the idea from to bring him here but it doesn't surprise me. Don't try to
give me any bullshit now. Just go and get changed and quickly; the
ref's wanting to start."

Whilst he trotted off without a further word the skipper turned
to me and I thought I might get a bollocking as well; he looked in the

mood for it; he was not just his usual amiable self. Instead, he just said, "We need to get you back to The Vale somehow."

"Here, John," said a bloke I knew by sight as he lived on the same road, "take my car," and he casually threw me a set of car keys. Yet again, I was veritably gobsmacked for the umpteenth time in my six weeks' acquaintance with The Vale as I knew the car in question was a brand new, racing green MGB Roadster which I had had the opportunity to admire from a close distance as it had passed me by on the road. I stood for a moment in a reverie and although I definitely was not thinking of taking a slightly longer route back to The Vale and giving a little tootle on the horn as I passed a certain young lady's house my momentary hesitation proved fatal.

"You have got a licence haven't you, John ?" asked the skipper; he was more of a stickler for detail than the car owner himself.

Handing back the keys, which I was going to do anyway, of course, I confirmed that my licence was still only a provisional one.

I arrived back at The Vale courtesy of someone who had gone to watch the first team but very kindly agreed take me back in his car. Fortunately, the opposition had been late arriving so I just managed to get on to the pitch in time for the kick-off in the Extra 'A' game. Had time permitted I would definitely have been a bit apprehensive as I lined up; I had already had a hectic debut. Even so, there was a fair amount of nervous energy to be released and I did a lot of running about to no great effect. I remember that game chiefly for the dearth of opportunities either to run like hell with the ball or to scrag my opposite number who, I was glad to note, looked comfortably small and puny and eminently scraggable. There was a lot of kicking by the half backs, usually into touch[16] so that the action was, basically, confined to the forwards and for most of the game the backs were

---

[16] *My first game with The Vale took place before the Australian Dispensation Law (1967): the ball could be kicked directly into touch from any part of the field and the lineout took place where it went in.*

little more than spectators. When the ball did come out the handling skills of the backs on either side did not seem all that good; passes went astray or were dropped. I didn't drop a single one but would have been glad of the chance. I had become resigned to the fact that my first proper game of rugby was going to end in a sense of anti-climax when our scrum-half, under pressure, as he had been most of the game, was pulled down as he made to kick the ball. He got his boot to it but I could see it was not going to find the intended touch so I chased off after it more for the sake of the exercise than anything. The ball bounced, eluding one defender, then bounced again eluding another and very conveniently bobbled over the try line as I arrived to pounce on it as eagerly as a leopard on a lost spot. Try! Brilliant! The scrum-half also looked very pleased with himself; I didn't realise it at the time but it must have looked like a planned move. Such things, I was later to learn, were a rare occurrence in the lower teams and planned moves that actually came off were more or less unheard of.

Soon afterwards the final whistle went and I was taken by surprise once more when our skipper suddenly shouted, "Vale, three cheers for Harlequins (or whoever it was we were playing, I forget now). Hip! Hip!" And we all hoorayed with gentlemanly enthusiasm. The opposition then reciprocated in similar fashion. Even then it wasn't finished; we all ran to form two lines, a tunnel through which the opposing players passed as we clapped them off the pitch. Hands were shaken and backs were slapped. "Well played", "Good game", and other compliments were expressed, sometimes with a particular recipient in mind, sometimes to the ether as sort of general comment. And yet still it wasn't over; they then formed a tunnel through which our skipper led us whilst they clapped and returned the compliments. I could not help but think how remarkably civilised it was. Thirty seconds earlier the two sets of forwards had been slugging it out as if trying to knock seven bells out of each other and now here they were slapping each other on the back as if they had just been for a walk in the park together and found a fiver[17] which they were going to share at the nearest boozer. I was forced to reflect on the difference from the local soccer league. Sometimes hands were shaken but it was not a universal custom; it depended very much on the individuals and how the game had gone which in turn depended on the referee and how robust or late he would allow tackles. It was not common but ill-feeling did sometimes carry on after the final whistle with insults being thrown or mud or even punches in a very extreme case. I found it difficult to imagine soccer players passing through a similar tunnel after a bad-tempered game without someone hissing, "Dirty bastard", or somebody's legs being taken from under them as they trotted through. It posed an interesting chicken and egg question if you stopped to think about it which I didn't; I was keen to get back to the clubhouse and see what happened next.

As I have mentioned the bath at The Vale was huge; I'd seen smaller front rooms in some of the local terraced houses. It was full of bodies by the time I got there and yet the capacity seemed somehow to be elastic; there was always enough room to squeeze one more in. Occasionally, somebody would find, on arriving, that there was standing room only and would exhort those at the far end to budge up a bit. Eventually a small amount of clear water would grudgingly be ceded somewhere and it would gradually make its way round to the newcomer.

It was soon obvious to me that the best places to be were round the edges of the bath where your ablutions could be carried out without being interrupted by passing feet or knees nudging your back. That tended to happen if you could only find a berth in the middle.

---

[17] *The days of the old white fiver which you folded up like a newspaper had gone and had been replaced by the "bluey" which had not the same majesty but was still impressive. With one of those you felt like you had hold of some real money – and you had – it would have bought more than 50 pints: more than enough for a good night out for two, fish and chips on the way home etc. The older reader may remember the record "Capstick Comes Home" (1981)?*

However, peering through the steam, I was able to spot where the two very best places were: the corners at the far end. There was no through traffic there and they were well away from the taps. You needed to stay clear of the taps. They were industrial units and the water fairly gushed out. If the water in the tank was at all hot it was very hot and those near the tap would be baling for all their worth to stop their privates getting scalded; they weren't too fussy where the water went. When the hot water in the tank had all gone the water from the tap suddenly went to freezing without any warning, prompting shouts of, "Turn the bloody thing off." But no one stirred, except to get away from the tap. There was always somebody in the vicinity of the tap, usually someone about to leave the bath anyway, who felt the need to demonstrate to the remaining bathers just how cold the water had suddenly gone. Like a demented dog digging for a bone, he would scoop the cold water over them until shouts suggesting he was a small female orifice who should depart the scene in a reproductive manner reached a crescendo. Then, just as it looked like two or three were actually beginning to stir themselves to deal with the miscreant, he would take himself off. Then somebody would have to blink and deal with the tap. But turning it off was no easy matter for you could bet that, whilst the water was hot, in order to ensure the maximum flow, some gorilla would have swung on the tap with all his weight so that it was jammed in the open position. The only way you had a chance of turning it was to grasp the wheel – it was a gate valve - with both hands and stand right up to it with one leg either side. That is to say you were not only standing in the cold water but it was gushing out and splashing up all over your nether regions. When you did get the wheel to start turning it did so agonisingly slowly; it was like trying to shut the watertight doors on the Titanic, only without the music. You would be turning away but the water would keep gushing in. It was a race against time: would you be able to stop the flow before your balls were frozen off?

But the guys in the far corner were unmoved by the weekly drama unfolding in front of them; they knew the cold water would reach them last and that somebody else would blink first. There they

52

sat, wedged comfortably in the corners as if they were on sun-loungers with the warm Caribbean lapping round them, legs stretched out, each arm resting along a side of the bath, a pint[18] in one hand and a fag in the other, the cares of the world evaporating with the rising steam. This was not just luxury; it was decadence and I liked it. I realised it must have taken some organising and I noted this for future reference; it was too late now for me to go and get a pint – I could hardly drip my way through the clubhouse and I didn't think for a minute I would have got served with just a towel round me. Clearly the trick was to get a pint whilst still dry and decent. I suddenly realised why rugby shorts, unlike soccer shorts, had pockets in them. Even so the logistics were quite complicated: you would have to be one of the first back to the changing rooms, take your boots off, purchase a pint with the ten bob note[19] in your pocket – obviously, you couldn't have coins - dash back to the changing rooms, place the pint in secure position where (a) no great ox-hoof might knock it over and (b) you could watch it so that no thirsty thief might help himself, strip off, grab your pint and your towel and get to the far corner of the bath before anyone else. I was filled with admiration for the two guys who had accomplished this feat and I was sparked with a great ambition: one day I would sit in one of those corners with a pint in my hand.

Befitting the standards to which the more affluent years were beginning to aspire, soap was provided in the bath. That is to say various pieces of soap were provided and whilst they didn't start off actually *in* the bath that was where they all ended up. Every now and then there would be a cry of "Who's got the soap?" Several people would have a fish round where they had last had some and sometimes,

---

[18] *These were the old style dimple or barrel glasses specially approved by Health and Safety for this purpose.*
[19] *Occasionally known as brown beer tokens these notes, which were the lowest denomination ever printed, were replaced by the 50p coin on Decimalisation Day: "bob" was a slang term for a shilling of which there were twenty to the pound.*

with luck, a piece would be found and passed to the enquirer. At other times several pieces would be discovered and chucked at him simultaneously so that he had no chance of ducking them all.

Now we are not talking about "fabulous pink Camay" here or "Cadum for madam"[20]: it was just basic soap of the same genus as that provided at the local swimming baths; it came in long bars and was cut up into lumps. After it had been in the warm water for a while it was just about soft enough to get up a sufficient lather to wash your hair with. This was something of a last resort: if the lather was not rinsed off again within seconds your hair set in a bouffant mass which kept for days whatever shape it left the bath in, defying the best efforts of comb or brush to persuade it back to normality.

In those days The Vale was not in the vanguard of male grooming; shampoo was catching on but not everybody remembered to bring it every week; some never remembered at all. A cry of "Who's got the shampoo?" would trigger a similar response to a request for the soap and would usually lead to somebody generously passing over a bottle of shampoo whilst its owner wasn't looking. Next thing the bottle would be seen floating somewhere on the surface obviously empty, whilst everybody would be smiling with squeaky clean hair. Eventually, the former owner would spot the floating object and a thought bubble would rise from his head, "That looks like my bottle of shampoo." Then his hand would surreptitiously snake out of the bath and feel for the bottle on the side of the bath where he had left it and another thought bubble would rise with "Oh fuck!" inside it.

In accordance with general procedure I followed my stay in the bath with a quick shower. The bath was to get the mud from the pitch off and the shower to rinse off the muddy water from the bath. Between the bath and the showers a mop and bucket were stationed for the use of the person requested by the skipper to chase the mud and grass round the bath and down the plughole when the bath was being emptied. I had noticed one or two using the bucket to clean their

---

[20] *Brands of soap which ran competing advertising campaigns on ITV and I dare say would be a hoot to see again.*

boots so I guessed it must be full of fairly filthy water. I was proved right a couple of minutes later when one reprobate got out of the bath and, for no apparent reason, tipped the whole contents of the bucket over someone in the bath he had been talking to moments earlier. Not only was the water filthy it must have been cold as well. I expected fireworks but, apart from the perpetrator hot-footing it into the changing room, nothing happened.

I finished my shower and went into the changing room where the perpetrator – I'll call him Stuart – was getting dressed. If it is possible to laugh your socks off at the same time as you are putting them on that is definitely what he was doing. As he was chuckling away to himself I wondered whether retribution might be on its way; it had all seemed too easy and I had spotted the big mistake: he had left the bucket at the scene of the crime. Obviously, his plan was to get dressed and get out of the danger zone as fast as possible; I had never seen anyone get dressed so quickly. I could see he had buttoned up his shirt wrongly in his haste but it wasn't the time to mention it. Then just as he got his blazer on I could see the changing room door behind him ominously starting to open slowly and I thought this is going to be touch and go. Then - I couldn't believe it - instead of staging a quick exit, Stuart sat down with his back to the door, lit a cigarette and started singing. He obviously thought that, having got his clothes on he was going to be safe but that wasn't the way I saw it for the door had opened wider and his victim – I'll call him Billy - was sneaking up on him with the bucket. He saw me looking at him and put a finger to his lips requesting my silence; I was the audience at the pantomime but, fair enough, I wasn't going to shout "He's behind you." It was nothing to do with me and I was far enough away from the impending action. Billy continued to sneak up on Stuart like a cat stalking a foolish thrush in full song. Stuart was oblivious. Although I could see Billy's brow was furrowed with the concentration involved in keeping his movements silent as he tiptoed up, even the intentness of his purpose could not stifle a grin of anticipated triumph playing round his lips. I had no doubt now that Stuart, clothed or not, was going to get it and he did: the whole bucketful. It put his fag out and he was soaked. He stopped singing. Billy said, "That'll teach you. You didn't think getting dressed was going to save you, did you?"

"I didn't think you'd go so far, you stupid bugger!" shouted Stuart but despite the fact that his clothes were soaking wet, possibly ruined as there was mud and grass all over his blazer, he seemed to be taking it reasonably well and then, suddenly, the pair of them burst out laughing so loudly that I dare say that had Billy had any socks on he would have laughed his off as well.

"That's what I like about you, Stuart," said Billy. "You're a silly bugger but at least you can take it as well as dish it out."

And he put his arm round Stuart in a worryingly tender moment. "But you were bloody daft," he continued, "to get dressed; you should have known me better than that. Look at the state of your..."

Suddenly the air was blue and thick with threats of murder, castration and disembowelment as the naked Billy chased Stuart round the changing room. Billy had just realised whose clothes Stuart was wearing.

By the time I got to the bar the queue was three or four deep. Those who had been spectating and thus not obliged to waste any time on ablutions were already nursing pints but they cheerfully made way as the players filed in.

"You get to the bar, lad. I'll bet you've got a thirst on after that."

I just could not get over how friendly and well-mannered everybody was. Blokes were peeling away from the bar at great speed, pints in hand and when I got there I realised why: the process of serving had been ingeniously mechanised. At the back of the bar pint glasses were lined up in rows, half-filled with lemonade. When anyone wanted a pint of shandy, which most of us did, these were just topped up with beer from a large jug and the serving was done in no time. Did these guys know what it was all about? Did they. Talk about the simple bare necessities; they were definitely coming to me.

The scrum-half insisted on buying me a pint which I received graciously. Whilst we were chatting another team-mate sidled up and said, "What I want to know is how did you know to start running when you scored that try?" This was said from the point of view that he had been playing rugby for years and it would never have occurred to him to waste energy running after a ball that someone else was much more likely to get to first. Had there been some kind of conspiracy between me and the scrum-half? As the truth was that I had just done it on the spur of the moment – it had seemed the obvious thing to do – I didn't really know what to say. I felt almost as if I had broken some unwritten rule and that I was going to be watched in future for any other signs of deviant behaviour. However, had I been perturbed I would not have been allowed to dwell on it for, suddenly, there was something else about the organisation to marvel at; a hatch opened in the wall to reveal several attractive and well-turned out young ladies hard at work in a kitchen. They were the Ladies Committee and they were just about to serve up a hot meal. I thought to myself, "Will this never end?" I was never able to eat a lot immediately after a game but a bowl of home-made pie and mushy peas was very tempting. "Red cabbage? Sliced onion? It's all on the table over there." My admiration continued to grow for this coruscating civilisation I had managed to discover with so little effort and which was so conveniently placed on my doorstep.

As it was the first match of the season everyone was intent on curing the withdrawal symptoms caused by the four month closed season[21]; the noise level in the clubhouse was growing exponentially with each pint consumed. Then someone managed to shout above the noise,

"Schooner race! Schooner race! Vale challenge Harlequins to a schooner race."

---

[21] *Despite the fact that all matches were then classed as friendlies no games between clubs were allowed between 30 April and 1 September without express permission from the governing body under threat of ex-communication. It was nice to have a decent break.*

This was the signal for tables to be moved and blazers discarded as the competitors from the two teams lined up. The noise level abated slightly as the umpire ran through the rules of engagement,

"Pints on the table, both hands behind your back until the previous person has finished his pint and put his empty glass on his head upside down. You must *drink* all your beer. No spilling or your team will be disqualified."

Number 1 for The Vale was impressive: a lanky lad who embodied hollow leg syndrome. Had he been as fast on the field as he was at drinking a pint he would have been a candidate for The Lions. It was like pouring it straight down an open drain; it hardly touched the sides and almost seemed like a waste. But they had some more than capable beer shifters on their side as well. It was neck and neck coming to the last pair who, with a fine disregard for the rules, picked up their pints and upturned them straight on to their heads. Both teams and their supporters claimed victory and proclaimed the other side as cheats. Amidst the uproar the umpire disqualified both sides and declared a draw: the usual result.

When the noise had once again died down a little somebody shouted,

"Come on, Vale! Let's give them a song."

There didn't seem to be any doubt amongst the old hands as to which song it was going to be for they were soon bellowing out:-

We are, we are, we are, we are the boys from down The Vale
We can, we can, we can, we can sup lots of ale
So come along and join us as we sit upon the floor
And we'll tell you lots of stories that you've never heard
before.

Although it wasn't in my rugby song book the lyrics compare favourably with the average contents thereof in terms of literary merit. The lines scan as well as rhyme. The metre and meaning are both strong and clear. The words are not difficult to learn; (even prop forwards have mastered them with relative ease). It rollicks along with gusto. But there is a flaw which is not immediately obvious although it is quite a big one; the problem is that the third line of the first verse – which is also the chorus - requires the choristers to actually sit cross-legged on the floor. Not only is this not recognised as a particularly good position for singing but you get your backside wet after the schooner race, you feel like a twerp and you look like a twerp. Were it not for the fact that you wished to show solidarity with your fellow twerps after consuming several pints, you would not entertain the idea. Of course, there is a very good reason for all this: 'floor' rhymes with 'before'.

The stories told in the following verses refer to the involvement, little known outside the club itself, of former Vale players in key historical events:

Godiva was a lady who through Coventry did ride
To show to all the populace the snow white of her hide
The only one that noticed that she rode upon a horse
Was a gallant rugby player from down The Vale of course.

(Chorus: as in the first verse – "We are, we are etc.

Napoleon thought that he would win the Battle of Waterloo
He also thought that Josephine was faithful and true
But at the battle Napoleon was taken from the rear
And Josephine was taken by a gallant rugby player.
From down The Vale, of course. (Chorus as before)

The final verse tended to be optional. It ran:-

There's a certain rugby union team in Lancashire today
That's thrashing all the opposition home and away

So be wary all you teams who still have got to play
Those gallant, dashing, handsome lads: the boys from down
The Vale.

It was optional because if you had lost and the opposition were still there it was a bit difficult to look them in the eye whilst you were singing this verse, especially, of course, when seated upon the ground, looking like the first form kids on the front row of a school photograph. Unfortunately, when someone looks like a twerp it is human nature to want to make them look a bigger twerp and it tended to encourage the opposition to think they could get away with throwing ale over you. That was always a mistake for when it came to chucking ale The Vale would stand up to the best.

Geronimo

Well, my stroke of luck in scoring a try on my debut for The Vale kept me out of the 'B' XV and in the Extra 'A' for the next match. I was on the wing again where I now fancied myself as a soaring eagle ready to stoop at the slightest opportunity. Unfortunately, I was also to become acquainted with the flipside to such predatory majesty: the starvation diet. This always threatens those at the end of the food chain and in my case the chain was made up of several pairs of less than the surest hands. I soon came to realise how complicated was the sequence of events before I might expect a run with the ball. First of all our forwards had to secure the ball and then release it to the scrum half which, in itself, was something which definitely could not be taken for granted. Then the scrum-half had to pass to the fly-half but the greedy little blighter regarded this as the last of all the other options available to him, which were to run himself, kick or knock on. And if he did pass, always assuming the fly-half caught it, he felt his first duty was to demonstrate how far he could kick the ball into touch. Only when he got bored with doing that would he think about throwing a pass to the inside centre. If the inside centre caught the ball he was keen to show he could kick it just as far as the fly-half (because he thought he should be the fly-half really which was why the fly-half didn't want to give him the ball in the first place). When he thought he had proved his point about kicking, the inside centre might have a run with it. First, he would try the inside break and slip through the door left slightly ajar by his opposite number to disappear into the waiting arms of the opposition pack. Next, he would try the outside break. This involved running towards the touchline at right angles to it until it became obvious even to him that he was not going to be quick enough to get round his man, then he would cleverly dodge back on the inside break and disappear once more into the arms of the waiting opposition pack. Some time into the second half the outside centre might get a pass and if he caught it there was the whole of his kick, inside break, outside break repertoire to be gone through before the eagle might be unleashed. It might look pretty good being an eagle and I reckoned I did look good with my shirt collar turned up slightly at the back following the style of one of the lady-killers in the first team and my gradually lengthening mane, which, released from the regime of school haircut regulations, was gradually developing the potential of flowing in my speedy wake, but most of the time I felt like a spare part. On a bad day the only thing that prevented boredom taking over completely was the throwing in at the lineout. I don't know what wingers in the lower teams do these days to stop themselves and their brains freezing up since some bright spark decided that hookers should take over the throwing-in duties. (Why? How unfair is that? Hookers have got plenty of other things to do and it's nice and warm in the middle of the scrum anyway). In those days it was always the winger's job to throw in and the ball was thrown underarm using both hands, like a lobbed pass. Of course, in order to be able to make a good throw you had to know which of your jumpers you were throwing for. Generally speaking, each side had three jumpers, one at the front of the line, one in the middle and one at the back[22].The pack leader decided where the ball was to go. He would tell the scrum-half who, by a clever, pre-arranged system of signals would pass on the message to the winger, all without the opposition knowing so that the element of surprise was carefully maintained. Essentially, there were three options to call for the throw: "front", "middle" or "back". I soon learnt that throwing to the back of the line was the least favoured option as The Vale forwards traditionally preferred a strategy of "Keep it tight, Vale!" and the back represented loose. And loose was dangerous; there was a danger somebody might get hold of the ball and run with it over to the other touchline. This was regarded as completely unnecessary work creation; there was nothing which could be done on the other touchline which could not be done just as well on the touchline you were already on, so what was the point of running all the way over to the other side of the pitch to do it?

---

[22] *Because lifting of the jumpers was not allowed the advantage of having the throw was not as great as it is today.*

The Vale had developed an ingenious set of secret signals to represent the three calls. These were "skin", "cloth" and "air". If the scrum-half had his hands on his knees or his thighs or put his finger to his nose then he was touching "skin" and the call was for the throw to go to the front of the line. If he had his hands in his pockets, on his shorts or shirt or, getting clever, was touching one of the forwards' shirts it was "cloth" and the call was for the middle and if he wasn't touching anything his hands were in the "air" which meant the throw was to go to the back. There was a fiendishly clever variation of this last signal: if the scrum-half put his hands on his head he was touching 'is 'air. (That is assuming he wasn't bald in which case I suppose it would have been skin but, although we had a Welsh scrum-half and two who were milkmen, we didn't have any who were bald, either by accident or design, so I never had the problem of working that one out). The fact that virtually every other club used the same set of signals didn't seem to matter. Having given the secret signal, the scrum-half would go and stand where he expected to receive the ball so that if the opposing forwards had not done so already they got a second chance to get the grey matter on to the job.

The younger reader might be surprised that the method of throwing in underarm persisted for so long but a lot of this was down to the balls: the weight and shape of them. Any newish balls were used by the first team. The thirds and fourths got the best of what was left. After a few seasons' use they would be bloated because the leather would have stretched and become porous. Given the slightest opportunity they would take in water like a dehydrated camel newly arrived at an oasis. There was no plastic coating on the leather even when new and definitely no pimples. As smooth as a baby's bum and as slippery as standard issue soap after half an hour in the bath, nobody could grip a wet ball in one hand, not even the really big guy with his hands like steam shovels. Torpedoes they were not. Even Alistair Campbell wouldn't have managed to get a spin on one.

The limitation of the underarm technique was that you had to lob the ball up and the further back down the line you had to get the ball the higher you had to lob it. The higher you lobbed it the more likely it was that the wind would blow it off course and the whistle would go for not throwing straight. In fact, sometimes it was virtually impossible to throw it straight to the back of the line; if there was any wind about at all it would bend like a non-Dutch cucumber. Some referees did take the view that if the ball was going straight as it passed over the middle of the line they would let it go but they were few. "Not straight" at the line-out was one of those black and white things which referees loved to use to assert their authority, just as they used to with "not straight" at the put-in at the scrum. (Another of life's little mysteries: why it no longer matters whether the put-in at the scrum is straight but it still matters at the throw-in?)

Added to that, practising the basic skill of throwing-in was a ball-ache; it consisted of standing on the try line at a distance from a goal post and aiming to hit an imaginary mark on it. It was like practising serving at tennis with just one ball. Even after you had done all that it was more or less impossible to get a full line-out of players to practise the real thing at midweek training as attendance from the lower teams could be a bit sporadic: more noughts than crosses. Whilst most first team players turned up for training most of the time even some of them did not turn up as often as they might have done. This could lead to problems with set moves on match days.

I enjoyed training; it got me out of the house, gave me a good work-out and the opportunity for a chat over a couple of quiet pints with the others at the clubhouse afterwards. A usual topic would be the game coming up on Saturday. The selection cards usually arrived on Wednesday morning, having been posted[23] on Monday evening after the selection committee meeting. However, anyone who had not received his card would be able to check the team sheets pinned to the notice board at the entrance to the clubhouse. One way or the other by the time we got to the bar after training on Wednesday evening we would all know who the opposition would be on Saturday. Although everybody had their own fixture list most did not bother to look at it

---

[23] *There was no second class mail. In most areas there were two deliveries of post on weekdays.*

again after the day they received it. That was a shame really for the fixture list was contained inside a hard-backed booklet in the club's colours, a neat little thing about 3"[24] square. It had all the information about the club's officials, vice-presidents (paying, non-playing members), the playing records over the years as well as the current season's fixture list. Because it doubled as a membership card it was designed to fit neatly inside the breast pocket of a blazer but it seldom seemed to find its home there, probably because we were never asked to produce proof of membership. I was sorry when the club decided to discontinue the booklet on the grounds of cost. It's strange that we are today, supposedly, better off than we were all those years ago; how did we manage to afford those little luxuries then, such as selection cards in the post and membership booklets?

The annual subscription for a playing member was five guineas[25] and the match fee was half a crown[26]. As a student I was expected to pay a reduced fee of only 1s.6d[27] and half the time I paid nothing as the person collecting the match fees would say, "You're only a student. I've got enough here to pay the "expenses[28]. You don't need to pay."

---

[24] *7cm approximately*

[25] *Five pounds and five shillings (£5.25). The guinea was the crafty counter to the £4 19s 11d (£4.99) ploy. With the latter the psychology was that it seemed less than a fiver but with the former it seemed like only a fiver but was actually 5% more. Decimalisation took place on 15 February 1971: prior to that there were twenty shillings to the pound, making a shilling worth five new pence. There were twelve pence to the shilling making an old penny worth something less than half a new penny.*

[26] *A crown was five shillings, making half a crown equivalent to 12.5p today.*

[27] *The equivalent of 8p which got you a pint of bitter at the club.*

[28] *At a home match the referee had to be paid his expenses, and the opposition's teas and jug of beer had to be paid for out of match fees.*

But even if I did have to pay what wonderful value it was: an afternoon and evening's entertainment, tea for next to nothing and really only your beer to pay for. And many a time the older players would buy you a pint. There was a disco every other week for a nominal charge and you didn't have to pay even that if you were on a "througher" i.e. you stayed down at the clubhouse after the game until the disco started. And plenty of girls came to the discos so you were spared the expense of going down town to look for them. Those simple, bare necessities[29] just kept coming.

The matches we played were all classed as friendlies. Initially, that was a strange concept to me but I quickly realised that even the word "league" was completely taboo in rugby union circles. Nevertheless, needless to say, some matches were more friendly than others. The match we had coming up one week early in my time at The Vale was against our local arch rivals, Colbourne. The conversation at the clubhouse bar the previous Wednesday evening after training reflected its status. Any sentence including the word "Colbourne" also seemed to include the words "dirty ... (take your pick of expletive)" and I am sure that the equivalent conversations taking place at the Colbourne clubhouse were similarly phrased. Results in Derby[30] matches often do not go according to previous form. A team may be gliding through a purple patch but can easily

---

[29] *The younger reader or prop forward should understand that here "bare necessity" is intended by the author as a figure of speech: we were at that time just getting used to the idea of oven ready chickens and peeled vegetables in supermarkets but the concept of ready peeled chicks as now seen strutting on our town streets on a Saturday night would have been beyond our wildest imagination.*

[30] *The origins of the term "Derby Match" are obscure. In 1829 a Frenchman watching a football match in Derby remarked, "If this is what the English call football what do they call fighting?". Others sources link the name to The Derby race meeting at Epsom because of the large crowd it attracted.*

slip on the banana skin such occasions may throw down. Conversely, morale may be low after a series of defeats but, sinews stiffened by the sight of the old foe, may bring out an exceptional performance. It was not so much the winning that mattered but not losing. That was the first objective: we must not lose; they shall not pass, they shall not score, give them nothing, don't take any chances. As long as they don't score we will always be in with a chance. The fear of losing in a Derby match was so much greater because, unlike the usual game it was not an event in isolation. Lose to a side the other side of the county and there was nobody to revive the memory of it for weeks afterwards; you were not going to bump into one of their players and be greeted with a smug smile. You were not going to be reminded at work, "I hear you lost to Colbourne the other week," especially by soccer fans who did not understand the scoring system, "You lost by *how* many?" And for once there might even be a match report in the local paper, especially if you lost.

There was a different atmosphere before the game the afternoon of my first local Derby. As soon as I went into the changing room I sensed the seriousness from the captain's stance: he had taken up position in the middle of the room and looked more like someone posing for a Spanish postage stamp than his normal genial self. He glowered at each new arrival to set the tone. "Come on, lads. Hurry up. Get changed. No messing about this week. Let's get on with it. Think about the game." A late arrival got a bollocking. Then came the team talk: "Right, lads. You all know who we're playing this week and you don't need me to tell you it's going to be a hard game. We've got to get stuck in from the first whistle. Have you got that? From the first whistle. No messing about. Not ten minutes into the game. Not five minutes into the game. In hard from the first whistle ..."

He was interrupted by a shout from the visitors' First XV changing room followed by a tattoo of studs on the floor and a roar:
"ONE ... TWO ... THREE ... FOUR ... ONE ... TWO ... THREE ... FOUR"

That, in turn, was followed by shouts from The Vale First XV changing room:

"We're going to have to watch it, lads; they've learnt to count since last time!"

"I heard they'd been having coaching."

"Still only got to four though!"

Our captain continued, "Forwards, we keep it tight. Tight! Have you got that? Tight! We secure our own ball and spoil theirs. Give them nothing. Backs, you've got to tackle everything that moves. Get in hard and bring them down. Whatever it takes. When we have the ball, this week, we keep it tight. Above all none of that fancy stuff we had last week!"

"What fancy stuff was that, skip?"

"Passing."

The pitches were in their best, early season condition; ideal for the open game of rugby we were not going to get. The early exchanges laid the marker, each side charging in fiercely. A Colbourne player got flattened in circumstances which encouraged their captain to take the unusual step of appealing to the referee for foul play. When this was ignored he marched up to Vale's skipper and shouted, "In hard, Colbourne!" The Vale captain stood his ground and without taking his eyes off his opposite number shouted, "In harder, Vale!" They then both stood, gut to gut, eyeballing each other like a couple of professional boxers before a world title fight. It always seemed like wholesale violence would break out but, in fact, it never did. In the end I think we just managed to win and despite it having been a scrappy game we were highly delighted.

Our game finished before the First XV game. We joined the spectators on the touchline and heard the bad news that Vale were losing 3 – 0. This was unexpected as Vale had won the last two encounters and had been playing well. Three wins on the trot would have worked wonders for the Vale lads in the bar afterwards; they might reasonably have speculated about the continuance of the fixture in view of Colbourne's inability to give them a game: a chance to twist the knife. There was no real question of the fixture being dropped, of course, but the mere suggestion would have been enough to raise the opposition's hackles and spoil their enjoyment of the McEwans. With home advantage The Vale had been definite favourites for a win that day but now time was running out and Colbourne were doggedly defending their slender lead. They were on the ropes but Vale could not land the knock-out blow. A last ditch tackle had halted a Vale attack inside Colbourne's twenty five yard line. Colbourne had scrambled the ball into touch but the tackler had obviously been hurt as he had failed to get up before the bucket and sponge had got to him. As we arrived at the touchline he was being resurrected with copious amounts of cold water down the back of his neck and wherever else the person wielding the sponge considered appropriate. Meanwhile, The Vale skipper had taken advantage of the man being down to call his pack and the scrum-half together.

"Right, lads! The ref says there are less than a couple of minutes to go. We have got to get a score or we will lose and we are not going to lose to Colbourne, are we?" (The lads were spot on in realising this was a rhetorical question so nobody said anything). We've got the throw-in and I'm going to call 'Geronimo'."

There was a sharp intake of breath from one of the senior players.

"Don't you think that's a bit risky, skip? We've only ever tried it once at training and ..."

"Shut up and listen! It's now or never. We've got to make this lineout count. They've worked out where our throws are going and they're waiting for us and spoiling; we've got to try something different. I'll call "skin" so they can hear it and they'll think it's going to the front but you (speaking to the scrum-half) call 'Geronimo' to confuse them. Don't give any signal; just call 'Geronimo'. Have you got that?"

There was no time for anything further to be said for there was a sharp blast on the whistle and the referee shouted,

"Come on, Vale! That's enough of that. Let's get on with it. What do you think this is? American Football? Lineout. Vale throw."

The Vale pack marched purposefully to the line, eyes straight ahead, trying not to look like conspirators but failing miserably. The Colbourne captain, who had been watching the huddle, smelt a rat.

"Watch them, 'bourne! Watch them! They're going to try something, 'bourne! Watch them! Watch them!"

And all the Colbourne team's eyes narrowed to slits through which they looked even more hostilely at the opposition. They were going to try something. It was tantamount to cheating at that stage of the game. Just what you would expect of The Vale. They couldn't just accept they were going to be beaten fair and square or try to win by playing honest, straightforward rugby. No. They were going to try and put some sneaky ploy over them. The rats! But what the hell were they going to do?

You could sense the panic building. Colbourne had got within a couple of minutes of an unexpected, face-saving victory through graft and grit and now there was a danger it was going to be whisked away from them in the dying seconds by some unknown, sneaky sleight of hand; some Fancy Dan stuff. Against the odds they had managed to hold The Vale all afternoon. Physicality held no fear; bodies would be put on the line regardless but the thought of being made to look foolish at the last by some devious trick was worse than the fear of losing itself. It was almost too much to bear.

"Watch them, 'bourne! Watch them!"

The nervousness had spread to the Colbourne supporters on the touchline. By contrast the Vale supporters were encouraged by the anticipation that The Vale still might have something up their sleeve and could yet come out on top.

"Come on, The Vale!" they shouted with renewed hope and vigour.

"Watch them, 'bourne! Watch them!"

"Come on, The Vale! Come on!"

The Vale winger strode up to the line, wiping the ball on his shirt and looked expectantly at the scrum-half for the signal. The scrum-half caught his eye and confidently shouted,

"Geronimo!"

"What the hell's that?" thought the winger.

He was one of those who was not an ever-present at training sessions and he had been missing the week when the move had been practised. The scrum-half noticed both the look of panic in the winger's eyes and the fact that he was looking intently at the scrum-half's hands, one of which was on his shorts and the other was free. He was looking for confirmation: which was it? Cloth or air? Realising what the winger was doing the scrum-half quickly hid his hands in his pockets, inadvertently giving the "cloth" signal but, realising this, even more quickly took them out again and made a signal at hip level waving both hands to show that didn't count - scrub that! Then he thought, by doing that, he might have given the air signal so he put both his hands behind his back and shouted again,

"Geronimo!" less confidently but more loudly.

A buzz went round The Vale supporters:

"They're going to do Geronimo! They're going to do Geronimo! Come on, The Vale! Come on!"

"Watch them, 'bourne! Watch them! They're going to do Geronimo! Watch them, 'bourne!"

Of course, none of the spectators on either side had a clue what Geronimo was. Neither did the winger. He realised that a move was being called but what the hell could "Geronimo" be? Then suddenly it clicked. There he was, standing at number two in the line with his unnaturally black hair, the deep tan which miraculously still persisted from the week's summer holiday months ago at Southport, the hatchet nose - he had to be Geronimo. And it all made sense: they would be expecting a throw to the back of the line to try to break the deadlock so the plan was to confuse them by throwing it to the front: a double bluff. That must be it. He had to get it right: it was vital. It couldn't be anything else, could it?

The tension had gripped the spectators; they had fallen silent apart from the odd half-strangled cry. The ref was looking at the winger now; he had to get the ball in or the ref was going to blow for delaying the throw. Geronimo was looking at him keenly too, obviously wanting to time his jump. The winger concentrated on

71

getting the right weight and trajectory on the throw to give Geronimo every chance of a making a two-handed catch and then, at last, up went the ball but, suddenly, the winger saw that Geronimo wasn't looking at him any more. He wasn't looking at the ball either; Geronimo had turned his back and peeled off and he was now running towards the back of the lineout. The winger's jaw dropped; he watched in horror as number three in the line peeled off to follow Geronimo, followed by four and five and six and seven with the scrum-half bringing up the rear like a pantomime dance routine. The Vale number eight was leaping like a spawning salmon to take the throw which would never reach him. It would have been a perfect throw if Geronimo had only stayed where he was; it gracefully reached the zenith of its parabola exactly where his outstretched hands would have cleanly gathered it in. Instead it was gratefully received by Colbourne's front jumper who, without pausing to question his luck, squirreled the ball under his arm and set off unopposed towards the Vale line like the biggest pixie you ever saw. There was nothing in front of him. On he charged only to be suddenly overtaken by an attack of agoraphobia. Finding himself alone with the ball in so much open space was too much for him. He panicked and punted the ball downfield. The Vale's full back was perfectly positioned – at the other end of the field, poised to take the scoring pass and the glory which Geronimo was supposed to bring. So there was no-one at home in defence. A Colbourne player won the race to the ball and scored gleefully beneath the posts.

Never again would Geronimo strike fear into the opposition ranks. And do you know what? Back at the clubhouse after the game the Colbourne players really rubbed it in. They did. Honestly.

Man down:
The Magic Sponge

Nowadays the top sides have at least one physio standing tracksuited at the side of the pitch who can be relied upon to produce all kinds of magic from his little black bag of tricks with which to treat an injured player or to make a telling contribution to his side's winning performance. In the era in which these tales began there was only one pitch-side remedy for injury: the magic sponge. For the duration of the game it remained completely neutral, offering its powers of healing to anyone from either side who might require them. At the beginning of the game it took up its station near to the halfway line, far enough from the touchline to avoid the collapsing maul but near enough to be of service when the time came, as it surely would. There it resided in splendid autonomy, floating impassively in a bucket of cold water. It belonged to no-one; it recognised no particular handler. If a press-ganged touch judge thought his position gave him any rights over the sponge he stood to be disappointed when the moment came.

The purpose of the sponge was not just to stop the water in the bucket freezing over on a cold day: it was used for removing mud from the eyes, for wiping dirt away from bleeding wounds, to revive the unconscious and as an infallible test for the seriousness of an injury: if you stayed down long enough for the man with the bucket and sponge to get to you it had to be bad[31]. In the typical case the man down would struggle to his feet like a groggy boxer beating the count, just in time to disappoint the bucket and sponge bearer by raising an

---

[31] *Play was always stopped if a man stayed down. Apart from the fact that everyone else welcomed a breather it seemed the decent and fair thing to do.*

73

outstretched palm as if about to hand off Dracula and protesting loudly, "I'm all right! I'm all right!"

(Of course, if you had mud in your eyes or were unconscious you couldn't see the rascal coming so there was nothing you could do about it).

I may have mentioned earlier that a sense of fair play permeated the era I am describing; The Vale religiously subscribed to that ethic. There was a simple protocol relating to the administration of first aid which had to be observed; only a person wearing Wellington Boots was allowed to be the bucket and sponge man. At any time after September, unless the winter rains came early, Wellington Boots were, of course, de rigueur for any spectator. And they were absolutely essential to negotiate the first fifteen yards or so of primeval swamp which extended inwards from the touchline. There, by night, the hippos frolicked and on Saturday afternoons the line-outs with their usually resultant scrums took place. Thus the sponge man was guaranteed a slow and slippery start. And, of course, he did not want to spill the icy water down his trouser leg so he struggled to get any speed up until he got his balance right. However, once he had gained the firmer ground, provided he avoided the odd crater created by the hippos' self- indulgent rolls and provided, of course, the quarry was still prone, the chance of homing in on the victim would encourage the sponge man to muster every yard of speed available to a man in an overcoat, wearing wellies and running across the equivalent of a ploughed field whilst carrying a bucket full of water. The arm carrying the bucket would be extended at full stretch so that the water, now sloshing over the sides of the bucket as he accelerated, would fall away from the carrier; then, abandoned to the thrill of the chase he would become careless of spillages, certain that enough cold water would still remain in the bucket at the end of his run for his sadistic purpose. For the sake of balance the non-carrying arm would be raised in what would have looked like a fascist salute had there not been a still smoking pipe clenched in the fist. Players and spectators alike would be enthralled by the suspense: was the man

74

down stirring, was he going to realise the danger in time? Ten, nine, eight ... a mental countdown would begin.

Of course, if you were daft enough to get injured in the hippos' play area on that touchline where the sponge lurked in its bucket you were easy prey. I remember once fielding an opposition kick ahead and watching with great satisfaction as my clearing punt sailed into touch sixty yards away. (Nowadays, since metrication, it would, of course, have gone almost ten per cent further). Then something hit me. He was so late I suspected that during the week he must have worked as a driver for British Rail[32]. Not only was I near the touchline but a former Vale player, who always turned out immaculately kitted-out to run touch, forgot himself in his excitement and, with a fine disregard for the protocol, grabbed the bucket and ran on in his studded boots. I had no chance. (I am glad to say that, shortly afterwards an enterprising Vale player, scandalised by what had occurred, prevented the possibility of a recurrence by divesting the touch judge of his laces on the pretext that he needed some tie-ups).

Now a non-rugby player reading this might think that the administration of the sponge was a simple matter which did not require a special technique; all that would be necessary would be to apply the cold, wet sponge to the affected part. Not so. The first thing any sponge man worth his salt did, regardless of any other consideration, was to squeeze the sponge down the back of the victim's neck. He would follow that immediately with another one down the inside of the front of the shirt. As the injured player gasped for breath the third spongeful went over his head and left him spluttering. Only at that stage would the question be asked,

"Where does it hurt?"

By then the man down normally could not remember.

Rugby shirts on cold, wet days act as a kind of primitive wet-suit. The water in the shirt gets slightly warmer on the inside from

---

[32] *British Railways had recently become British Rail in an attempt to change its image but it remained nationalised. It had a reputation for running trains which often arrived late and were overcrowded.*

body heat. It may not be much but it is a small consolation. However, once somebody has poured cold water down the front and back of your shirt you have lost that tiny comfort for the next ten minutes; it gives you something else to worry about and helps to take your mind off the injury. However, more importantly, we can see here where the true value of the magic sponge lies: once you have been properly sponged on a biting cold day you never forget the experience so that the next time you get hurt you get to your feet quickly and convince yourself it isn't so bad.

The Original

*"There are dim and dismal days in February
That are fit for nowt but supping."(Anon)*

February. What a month! The spiritual warmth engendered by the festive season has already dissipated in the early weeks of January, dissolved into the darkness, leaving nothing to look forward to even on the dim, distant horizon . Work starts and finishes, cheerlessly, in the night-time; the days have been too short for too long; the cheering yellow of the daffodils is not yet to be seen and the first day of spring still too far away to imagine. Meanwhile the weather is and will, for many a week, remain atrocious. February fill-dyke. To the Romans it was the month of purgation. To the Anglo-Saxons it was mud month. To The Vale it was a kind of muddy Purgatory; something to be got through before better weather and Easter's[33] promise came around.

In a good year the home pitches were only ankle deep in cold, clinging, black mud pocked with boot marks full of a dirty grey soup, presenting a scene which would have been reminiscent of the primeval swamp had it not been so lifeless and cold. Even the hippos were in hibernation. February challenged your loyalty to the game, especially if you were blessed with the imagination to think of anything else to do on a Saturday afternoon. Repent of this foolishness; stay in the pub. No. Be a man; turn out for The Vale!

Mothers and wives would complain about the mud-sodden kit brought home to be washed. Tipped out of the spattered kit bag the contents looked like some agricultural process that had gone terribly wrong.

"You can put that lot to soak in a bucket and make sure you rinse it off properly before it goes in the machine."

---

[33] *Easter meant touring time. With the increase in disposable income i.e. beer money, it was just becoming traditional for even junior clubs to tour every two years, playing host in the intervening years.*

"And don't you even think about washing those boots in the sink."

There were some players who did not even think of washing their boots at all. After the match they went into a dirty polythene bag which kept the mud off the towel and they stayed there till the following week, out of sight, out of mind, festering in their muddiness. You might just about get a season out of a pair of boots treated this way. The colour would leach out of the uppers where they joined the sole signalling a threat to part company but the laces would rot first and break some time after Christmas. It always seemed to be the players who were not changed and ready to go out until the last minute whose laces "went" in that final act of preparation, the drawing tight of the laces. And they always snapped at the last eyelet at the top of the tongue. If only one end of the lace went it was possible to save the situation by re-threading but if both ends went at the same time under the strain of pulling you were knackered.

"Oh shit! Anybody got any spare laces?"

"I've got one. It'll cost you a pint."

Sometimes there were no spare laces and the captain, wanting to give his pre-match pep talk would growl unsympathetically as the quest continued;

"Anybody got some tie-ups they can lend me then? Come on Mick. You've got some decent, long tie-ups on. Lend me them, will you?"

"On your bike. What do you think I've got them on for? My socks won't stay up without them."

"Bloody poser! Come on! I only need one ... Anybody?"

If nothing could be found or scrounged the only thing for it was to miss out the last two pairs of eyelets and try to tie a knot further down the boot with the little bits of lace that were left. Of course, the insecure boot always came off at some stage during the game, sucked in by the quagmire, and the game would stop whilst it was recovered, emptied of mud and squelchily restored to its owner's foot as the referee muttered impatiently. At this stage if one of the touch judges was wearing boots he would be expected to do the

78

decent thing even if it meant hobbling up and down the touchline for the rest of the afternoon as he tried to keep his laceless boots on his feet.

I remember an elderly gentleman once diverting a conversation he had insisted on having with me to the subject of February. Having established his theme, he withdrew from his pocket a creased and rather grubby piece of paper which he proudly unfolded to show me; it was the manifesto of his life's mission. At the top of the page was typed the familiar little rhyme:-

"Thirty days hath September
April, June and November.
All the rest have thirty one,
Excepting February alone
Which has twenty eight."

So there it was, straight away: February was an exception. Standing out like that put it clearly in the firing line. He looked me straight in the eye, checking the point had gone home. I nodded as if to say, "Fair enough; I wouldn't argue with that."

"February is a dreadful month," he said. "Wouldn't we all be better off without it?"

How could I not agree? I nodded that through as well.

"Aren't the days longer, the weather much better in May, June, July and August?"

I nodded yet again.

"So the answer's simple: we abolish February and add one week each to May, June, July and August."

On the Saturday afternoon where this tale begins the Vale lads would have voted, to a man, for the abolition of February. They had begun to congregate inside the clubhouse to wait for the coach to take them to South Hoddlesdale. They did not need to look out the window to see the rain coming down like heavy duty stair rods[34]. They could hear it most of the time, drumming on the corrugated asbestos roof of the clubhouse and crackling on the big window which looked out on to the pitch. The only reason they could not hear it all the time was due to fluctuations in the volume of the howling of the wind. If they had looked out of the window they would have seen two ducks; their proprietorial air suggesting they had always owned the first team pitch which lay beneath the watery expanse on which they floated. It's an amazing thing: as soon as a puddle's diameter becomes more than two metres it is colonised by a pair of ducks who manage to look, somehow, as if they have always been there. Nobody sees them arrive and nobody knows where they come from or go to. They are just there. I bet when Noah dropped the plank they were already waiting.

The home games at The Vale had been called off days ago. Just like they had been the previous week. This had caused normal selection to be revised; only those who were desperately keen to have a game were considered. South Hoddlesdale had telephoned to say they only had one pitch fit to play and had suggested that if The Vale really wanted to play they should send a XV of around second team strength. Nevertheless, even amongst what we may presume were some of the keenest rugby playing souls there were misgivings and mutterings:

"Are you sure we're going to play? I don't fancy travelling all the way up there just to come back again."

"It's been raining all night," said another. "Look at the state of it out here! Is it going to be any better up there?"

"Has anybody rung them?"

"Yes. Bill rang again not ten minutes ago. They say it's on."

"They've got a good pitch up there. Drains well."

"You don't think they're going to let us play on the first team pitch, do you," said an old hand. "Wreck it for the rest of the season.

---

[34] *In the days before fitted carpets became the norm a special length of stair carpet was held in place by long, brass rods which the lady of the house always kept shiny with "Brasso".*

No. I reckon we'll be playing on that shit-heap they keep for special occasions."

"What? You mean that one that's about half a mile from the clubhouse?"

"That's the one."

"Quick. Ask the steward for some bin bags to sit on then we can get the coach to take and fetch us."

"Forget it. After the last time we did that the coach company said we're banned if we try it again."

The journey to South Hoddlesdale was a quiet one. The coach was more than half empty so everybody spread out, not seeking conversation. The rain was still lashing down. The wipers swished hypnotically. The mood was subdued. It seemed even the liveliest spirits were dampened by the weather. Nobody bothered to pull the usual gag of asking for passports as we passed into Yorkshire. Literally adding to the gloom were no less than four serious pipe smokers. The younger reader may never have seen one but then every team had one, sometimes two who seemed as if they had been born with pipes hanging out of their mouths. However, to get four on the same coach was one of the unforeseen and unhappy results of the day's selection policy. It would not have been so bad if they had all sat in one row, like the four funnels of the Titanic, but as it was one sat in each corner and they puffed away like Battersea Power Station in its pomp. There was nowhere to escape. If you were one of those who could not stomach any food after breakfast on match days you certainly did not want to be engulfed by clouds of pipe smoke. But to smoke a pipe was a man's right, a real man's right and the smokers would not have considered putting out their pipes even if asked nicely, which, of course, they were not. There was a more or less established form of exchange which never altered anything except possibly to make the non-smoker feel better for having had a grumble:-

"What the hell have you got in that bloody pipe?"

"That's my business."

"I can tell that. But how do you dry it?"

81

Other variations on the theme proved equally futile.

At that time pipe-smokers considered themselves superior to non-smokers and those who smoked cigarettes. They had that air about them. The serious pipe smoker always had one thumb with a nasty, nicotine-stained nail. The end of this "tamping" thumb was thickened, blackened and scorched and, apparently rendered insensitive to heat through repeated abuse. It was used with macho aplomb to extinguish the smouldering tobacco prior to the pipe being nonchalantly stored away in a side pocket. On one occasion, having accomplished this manoeuvre a few moments earlier with a flourish of which a member of The Magic Circle would have been proud, The Vale's most serious pipe smoker of all time spontaneously combusted as he chatted at the bar. Smoke and flames were observed issuing from the oblivious wearer's jacket pocket and he had to be extinguished by means of a soda syphon[35] and a waterfall of generously donated beer and then smothered with wet bar towels by other well-wishers. For all of which he was duly ungrateful.

Whilst I would not say that there were a lot of pipe smokers at The Vale the steward used to panic when stocks got down to the last half hundredweight of St. Bruno.

The coach rocked as it was blasted by the wind along the exposed stretches of road and now and again a hail of broken twigs clattered against the windscreen. Finally, it lurched and splashed its way through the potholes in South Hoddlesdale's car park. We picked up our bags and filed in. The clubhouse had not been open all week. It was damp and smelt of stale beer and cigarette ash. Nevertheless, it was a small improvement upon the now heavily polluted atmosphere we left behind on the coach. A coal fire had only just been lit and despite the howling gale outside seemed to be struggling to get going. Lacking any incentive to dally, we made our way through to the

---

[35] *This was an item which stood on the bar in more civilised times in any reasonable licensed establishment for the free dispense of soda water into one's whisky or brandy.*

82

visitors' changing rooms. These were cold, unwelcoming and smelt of rancid olive oil and wintergreen mixture, Sloan's liniment and other miracle-working potions.

South Hoddlesdale's ground was in a wonderful setting, overlooked by a mighty crag: a typical Dales landscape. But like most landscapes it looked better in the sunshine. The timber construction which served as the clubhouse had the appearance of a large, second-hand Scout hut. Earlier generations of rugby players had done their best with limited resources and their own hands to provide the facilities. Although, in the depths of winter, it was not an outwardly hospitable place it had its compensations. A warm welcome was guaranteed from the 'Dale players and the Spartan changing rooms were equipped with ablutions which possessed unusual restorative properties. There were several small baths[36] served by an interesting system of pipework of Heath Robinson design but the real charm lay in the concreted bases of the baths themselves. These were also, no doubt, the product of earlier DIY and the trowelled surfaces of the screed had begun to wear away, exposing the grit beneath. The slightest movement whilst seated guaranteed the removal of clinker, dangledoggies and even, it was rumoured, piles. The venue was always a popular away fixture.

"Just a minute," said one veteran. "I'm going to make bloody sure they've got the water heating up for the baths before I start getting changed."

It seemed a wise precaution but when he came back, nodding affirmatively, there was nothing else for it. We got changed.

We were, indeed, destined to play on the occasional pitch towards which we straggled off in small groups with as much enthusiasm as we could muster, straightening up when we saw the opposition, although we were consoled to note they did not look any

---

[36] *Almost every rugby club had a bath or baths in a variety of different sizes and constructions. I always felt cheated if we came to a club where they only had showers. The danger of the transmission of the AIDS virus has sadly done away with the institution.*

happier than we did. The pitch had obviously been in use the week before: such grass as remained had long since given up any hope of maintaining itself erect and it merely lay in the mud in strands or yellow green patches, dreaming of spring. The blurred lines of whitewash were broken here and there where muddy puddles had defeated the line marking machine. The rain slashed into these puddles barely provoking a response from the dark, viscous surface. The line flags leaned at different angles, the sodden, lifeless soil indifferent to whether they stood or fell as long as it was not required to support them.

In the time it had taken to walk to the pitch, shirts were already soaked and were shrinking like some grotesque, striped cling film to the contours of the interesting variety of torsos beneath them. This was a temporary phenomenon for shortly the sheer weight of water they absorbed would stretch them out again, producing long sleeves which dripped from the cuffs and a soggy flap at the front which hung down from all but the most protruding of midriffs. We had the second team shirts that day. They had been cast off by the first team at the end of the previous season and so were still, mostly, in good condition, being only three years or so old. Even the first team did not yet aspire to numbered shirts so there was the usual free for all when the shirt bag was tipped out on the dressing room floor. Those who had rummaged successfully to find a shirt that fitted them soon surrendered the greater part of that advantage to the effects of the deluge. Those who had not been so fortunate in the lucky dip were represented by an Incredible Hulk impersonation in the scrum and a winger who looked like a striped teepee had collapsed round him.

The referee, under the crafty pretence of straightening the corner flags, had managed to sneak up on the two local spectators. Dalesmen are not easily inconvenienced by a little weather. Despite the conditions they had turned up to see who would end up cocks of the midden that afternoon and now they were going through their pockets trying to find a clean handkerchief to use as a flag, having been cajoled into service as touch judges.

The referee, we later discovered, turned out to be not only as keen as mustard but also the fittest man on the park. He had only recently retired from playing, still relatively young, due to an injury. He was rumoured to have played at County level[37] and whatever the injury might have been it had nothing to do with his legs or lungs. He was everywhere. It was not the question, as it often was, of some overweight sexagenarian gasping like a beached walrus in a vain effort to keep up with play; at times he almost seemed to be ahead of it. He popped up in places he had no right to be and spotted infringements that normally went undetected. He was not minded to make any allowance for the conditions and at the slightest suggestion of a fumble[38] he blew up for a knock-on. Before the first ten minutes had gone he had become known, out of earshot, as "Whistle Happy", the final ingredient in the day's recipe for hypothermia. For the backs that was; meanwhile the forwards were to have a whale of a time: one scrum after another with hardly any distance to run between them.

The visiting backs had been allowed the use of the match ball for their warm up. Had the ball been human it would have been classed as morbidly obese. By the time the referee called the two captains to the middle it was the same blunt, drab brown as the pitch and if you listened carefully you could hear it sucking in the moisture, making a noise like one of the serious pipe smokers bidding a fond but temporary farewell to his beloved pipe. Even so, the backs were sorry to see it go as it was punted up for the start; further opportunities to fondle its voluptuous curves would be scarce over the next eighty minutes. For eighty minutes it was to be; Whistle Happy would have

---

[37] *In the days before leagues were introduced into rugby union, representative honours for the County were highly sought after by ambitious players and were one of the main routes to national selection. The County Championship was taken very seriously in most parts of the country with the possible exception of the South East.*
[38] *The so-called cricket catch was not introduced until the 1970s. Until then the slightest "readjustment" constituted a knock-on.*

nothing of the captains' joint petition that half an hour each way might be enough and he did not offer the usual compromise of thirty five.

Because it was a scratch side I found myself playing, by default, at inside centre, a position where I was never comfortable: whenever I got the ball there never seemed to be any space but when my opposite number got it there seemed to be acres to cover. The consolation that the chances of receiving a pass were higher by a factor of at least eight than on the wing, where there was more of a chance of getting frostbite, was tempered by the fact that from a distance my opposite number looked very large and distinctly useful.

The whistle went to start the game and we in the backs showed willing: we took our hands out of our pockets and lined up flat when it was their put-in at the scrum or throw-in at the lineout and ran with purpose towards our opposite numbers when the ball came out on their side. But when it did their scrum-half either fumbled it – whistle, "Knock-on. Scrum" - or passed it out to their fly-half who either fumbled it - whistle, "Knock-on. Scrum." – or kicked it into touch.

When it was our put-in or throw-in we took our hands out of our pockets and lined up deep so that we could each get a better view of our scrum-half or fly-half taking turns to fumble it or kick it. Meanwhile the forwards were in their element. Within ten minutes of the start they were all the same shade of dreary brown as the pitch from top to toe. At least they were keeping warm. The sweat of honest endeavour combined with last night's beer and curry in a cloud of rising vapour which went five yards forwards, five sideways and five backwards as it hovered above a sprawling, grunting mass which, fascinatingly, never failed to locate the next morass just before the whistle went. The half- time oranges arrived before either side had got the ball beyond the stand-off. There had been no kickable penalties as all the action had taken place within ten yards of the touchline between the twenty five yard lines[39]. Besides, although the referee was

---

[39] *When metrication was introduced into rugby union the 25 yard line became the 22 metre line but at the same time the five and fifteen yard lines became five and fifteen metre lines.*

always on the spot he often could not tell who was doing what to whom anyway because all the shirts were the same muddy colour. Had there been a scoreboard it would not have been troubled.

The second half continued in the same vein except that the fly-halves were now standing a little closer to their scrum-halves who, as their arms tired and the ball's weight continued to increase, were having difficulty heaving it out. The other backs, in order to avoid lapsing into cold-induced unconsciousness, had begun running ever more eagerly towards the opposition when the ball emerged, even though it was a foregone conclusion that it would not progress beyond number ten. On one occasion our fly half dummied a pass to me before deciding to kick anyway. This gave my opposite number the excuse to smack me to the ground, dirtying my shirt and shorts which I had managed to keep clean until then. The beast. I couldn't help noticing that he was around six inches taller and a couple of stones heavier than me and I felt like telling him it would be fairer if he went and played in the forwards. But at least the way he had charged in, like an enraged bull at a matador, encouraged me to think he might be susceptible to a little shimmy. However, by the time we got to the final quarter there seemed to be so little chance of both our scrum-half and fly-half catching the ball and delivering a pass that I had given up even speculating what I might do if I ever got the ball. Roll on the final whistle.

As the match dragged on to its seemingly inevitable, scoreless conclusion my opposite number was becoming visibly more frustrated and agitated. Unlike me, it looked like he still harboured hopes of a pass. He had obviously formulated the opinion that he would have no trouble getting past me to set up the winning score if only he could get his hands on the ball. I was worried he might well be right as I had noticed he seemed to move pretty quickly for a gorilla. He and their fly-half were having increasingly heated altercations each time the fly-half failed to get the ball out to him. Although I couldn't hear, from a distance and in the wind, what they were saying, their voices were raised and they were gesticulating to one another; it looked like either they were going to try move number two or they were fairly pissed off with each other.

We had been camped just outside their twenty five yard line for most of the second half but as full time approached their forwards were beginning to look a shade fitter than ours. They were inching their way up the touchline and looked capable of making a breakout. A win for us would, obviously have been better than a draw but to lose at this stage would have been so much worse. By now the referee was looking at his watch at ever decreasing intervals and so it seemed we would avoid that catastrophe. But then the dreaded moment came. The ball was in and out of their scrum as if their scrum-half had it on elastic. It flashed through the fly-half's hands and on to the inside centre who took it at speed. He didn't have the decency to threaten a side-step or even to offer me a face-saving, slight swerve; he just came straight on at me and right in the middle of the pitch too. Everybody was watching. All I could see was the top of his head and his knees going up and down like the pistons on The Flying Scotsman. To make it worse I had been appointed captain of our makeshift side for the day. Even though the greasy surface might have provided a pretext I could not afford to slip then dive, arms flailing in frustration and failure. I was the skipper, The Vale's skipper; I had to do something and it was going to have to be a head-on tackle. I launched myself. It was not one of those "hits" the commentators talk about on television. Nor was it the classic tackle where the tackler's arms slide down around the runner's legs then tighten and down he comes like a mill chimney toppled by Fred Dibnah's dynamite. In fact, I am not sure how you would describe it but I made contact and then managed to put into practice the coaching of one of the Vale ancients on the subject of last-ditch tackles: "ger 'old o' summat and keep'old".

At first I thought he was going to drag me all the way ignominiously to our try line but finally he began to stumble and down we went in a heap. The ball went loose[40] . As we both scrambled for it my left

---

[40] *The law was then that if you were tackled, brought to the ground and held you had to release the ball immediately.*

elbow somehow came into contact with his right cheek. Nevertheless, despite this inconvenience, he was on his feet before me and, as soon as I got up and without allowing me any opportunity whatsoever to apologise, he took an almighty swing. The referee who was, incredibly, already standing behind me would have been decapitated had he not also ducked. The blast on the whistle, which was delayed for a few moments as the referee recovered his stature and composure, was loud and shrill.

"Penalty to Vale. Any more of that and you'll be off[41]."

"But, ref, he ... "

The whistle went again.

"Ten yards," said the referee, advancing up the field and standing on a spot with his arm raised ten yards further up the pitch from where he had awarded the original penalty.

"How long to go, sir?" I asked.

The referee looked at his watch.

"It's full time. You can take the penalty. But that will be it. You've got up to two minutes if you want to kick at goal."

In no time at all I had worked out the best option: I said we would take the kick and looked round to summon our kicker. Then I remembered we hadn't got one; it was down to me. However, thanks to the extra ten yards we were inside their half, right in the middle of the pitch and the wind was strengthening behind. There was nothing to lose. I built up the earthworks as high as I could[42], lined the ball up

---

[41] *The unwritten rule used to be that a punch which connected got you a warning that you would be sent off next time. If the punch did not connect, as most didn't, it didn't count. You would, of course, go straight off for striking the referee but possibly not if it was unintentional.*

[42] *First it was pint pots full of sand then came the plastic tees but at that time you had to make do with whatever you could produce with your boot heel.*

with the posts, and measured out a long run. I ran up, took a mighty swing and kicked the ball as hard as I could. As it buffeted its way through the air all eyes were on the flight and each split second twenty five brains made feverish forecasts of success or failure based on calculations of height, distance, trajectory and wind-speed. Not to be left out the front row forwards furrowed their brows and feigned concentration. The ball had taken off like an overweight threepenny[43] rocket. Then the wind had got hold of it and lifted it. On and on it flew turning slowly like a fat little piglet on a spit. It was looking good, going straight as a marrow but suddenly the wind dropped and it died like a barrel rolling off the dray. I would have liked to have been able to say that it just had enough momentum to bounce on the crossbar on its way over but I cannot tell a lie: it sailed over by at least a clear inch and a half. Up went the referee's arm as he whistled. He had been standing under the posts; in the circumstances and in the gloom, there was no danger of him relying on the eyesight of the local touch judges. More short blasts on the whistle signified the end of the proceedings bar the cheers and handshakes. Jubilation and despondency, those twin impostors each claimed fifteen souls, to possess them, with ever diminishing power, for one week only but I can still imagine the roar of the crowd to this day.

In the bar afterwards my opposite number and I got round to exchanging pints. Similar situations have often led to life-long friendships. Sadly, it was not to be in our case but as I was leaving he said he was looking forward to playing against me in a return fixture at The Vale. Which was nice of him.

---

[43] *Old pence, of course, prior to decimalisation in 1971. Threepenny rockets were the cheapest you could buy. There was never any danger of them going into orbit.*

Up The I.R.A!

Just as every rugby club is the same but different every tour is the same in principle but unique in the detail. And every tour is the tour to end all tours. Until the next one. The Vale tour to Ireland was no exception. It took place when The Troubles, as they were called by the Irish with typical understatement, had begun to surface once again. However, after the success of The Vale's earlier overseas tours which had started, daringly, with the Isle of Man before taking on M. Le Frog in his own backyard, a few bombs here and there were not going to dampen enthusiasm for the forthcoming Easter Tour. Besides, the players had complete confidence in the organising committee. They were sure that they would have considered all the angles; if they had decided there was nothing to worry about that was good enough for them; no need to give it another thought. Fund-raising discos and events had been held; the beer money had been saved; there was never any doubt that the tour would go ahead. In any event, all the problems were in Northern Ireland and they were going to be playing in the South which was totally different. Quite early on Good Friday morning their ferry docked at Larne, which the majority of the tourists discovered for the first time, was just north of Belfast.

The trip had begun in fine style the previous afternoon. Most of the tourists had met at The Vale clubhouse where they had taken the opportunity of getting in some last-minute training by sampling a pint or two of the Guinness. They knew, of course, that the English Guinness was inferior to the Irish Guinness as it was the first thing you were told by anyone who had been to Ireland, "It's the Liffey water, you know; makes all the difference." But The Vale were a practical lot and were accustomed to making best use of whatever resources were available.

Such was the sense of anticipation that the coach was able to get away on time. Other tourists were to join the coach en route and it was not long before the first stop was made. One of those joining the party seemed reluctant to get on the coach so keen was he on prolonging his farewells to his beloved; it earned him another bird in the process which he got in the time honoured manner from those already on the coach, impatient at the delay.

On arriving at the docks, the size of the "boat" took many by surprise. From the quay it looked enormous, way over the top; they were only going to Ireland after all. The ferry was, in fact, a cargo vessel which had a number of cabins for foot passengers. It was an economical means of crossing, devoid of frills; the passengers boarded on to a lower deck via a gangplank. There were no other passengers and preparations for departure began as soon as the touring party had embarked. I had scarcely stowed my bag in my cabin when so much shouting and raucous laughter suddenly broke out on the top deck that I shot up there like a scalded cat; something was going on already and I wasn't going to miss it.

In order to leave the docks the boat had to execute a U-turn. This was achieved by putting on the nautical equivalent of a full lock to the right and pushing away from the quay by the stern; the bows were just beginning to part company with the dock as I reached the top deck. The cause of the uproar was immediately obvious: the tourist who had caused the delay en route now appeared as a lonely figure on the quay. A rumour quickly spread, incredible to the younger, unattached tourists, that he had delayed boarding to go to a call box[44] to telephone his beloved whose side he had only so recently left. However, it looked like he would soon be able to convey any further messages in person as he seemed destined shortly to become an ex-tourist; the record-holder for the shortest tour ever; a partaker of the metaphorical early bath; a person who had literally missed the boat. The irony that he was a referee was not lost upon those gathered present and was, indeed, freely referred to. But not having his whistle on his person, he was obliged to use other means to endeavour to

---

[44] *The younger reader is reminded that mobile phones did not then exist. The G.P.O. (see earlier footnote) provided boxes in strategic places which contained coin operated telephones and which also occasionally served as emergency urinals.*

attract the attention of someone who might be willing and able to assist him. In fairness, when faced with such a situation, especially when one is the author of one's own misfortune, it could be difficult to hit upon the right words without wishing to appear coarse or rude but "I say!" did appear a little weak to the spectators, thus earning the latecomer the other half of his brace of birds for the day. It may be, however, that this exclamation, repeated in quick succession several times from different positions up and down the quay with increasing urgency, volume and pitch was ultimately successful in attracting the attention of a crew member or it may have been the hullabaloo from the top deck where the rest of the touring party was by then assembled to a man. Who knows? But a crewman did appear at the stern and the man whose tour hung in the balance took up station on the quay in expectation of the gangplank being lowered again to accommodate him. But the crewman opened a little gate in the stern rail and threw down a rope ladder. It looked to be a newish rope ladder. It looked to be a strong rope ladder in good condition but there was no getting away from the fact that it was a rope ladder. It was a very long rope ladder at that. The candidate for the shortest tour on record surveyed the situation carefully. Despite the fact there was no lack of advice and encouragement it would be fair to say that he did not appear to be rarin' to go and it looked like odds-on a refusal at the first. He made a second survey of the situation. It was a matter of fifteen feet down from the level of the quay to the water which was churning like a maelstrom under the action of the propeller. The distance from the quay to the rope was small but gradually increasing as the bows began to swing round. The racket had ceased as the drama had gripped the spectators. Would he? Wouldn't he? The would-be passenger looked up at the crewman and enquired plaintively, "Can't you bring it a bit nearer?" A noise which would not have disgraced the reception of a championship winning try in injury time erupted. The crewman declined to comment. The gap increased a little more. As some literary person once remarked, the time had come. It was do or die; either literally on the one hand or of shame on the other. And then, suddenly, he did; he leapt and seized the rope in both hands whilst

93

both feet landed on a rung. Indiana Jones it was not for we were denied the fallible foothold and the suspense of the dangle in mid-air but full credit was due for some splendid entertainment. Spontaneously, the touring party burst into a song of praise:-

Why was he born so beautiful
Why was he born at all
He's no bloody use to anyone
He's no bloody use at all
Without his pants on (descant)
He's no bloody use at all.

We could hardly have hoped for a more inspiring start. How long was the rope ladder? Two choruses had been completed before our hero reached the safety of the deck.

The night passed without any further incident worthy of being reported as the ferry sailed over the Irish Sea which was as calm as a baby's top lip. When we docked at Larne early in the morning a blue and white Ulster Bus would have been waiting for us to take the tourists on the next part of our journey had it not been late. It looked a bit decrepit when it did arrive and it was definitely a bus rather than a touring coach; rather uncomfortable for anything more than a short journey. The engine didn't sound too good either.

Passing through the outskirts of Belfast, the sight of rows of burnt out buildings did nothing to raise spirits: it was a little early in the morning for that kind of thing. One of the intelligentsia at the front of the coach proclaimed, "It's been going on for centuries, you know. The Battle of the Boyne was in 1690 and ..." We didn't know. We didn't really want to know. It was sectarian violence between Catholics and Protestants. There were members of both denominations on the bus, at least in theory, and that was a matter of no consequence whatsoever. The Troubles were nothing to do with us; we weren't religious bigots, just rugby players going on an Easter tour.

By the time we got to Dungannon it was clear the bus was not going to make it any further and we had to get off and wait for a replacement. Easter tour, Good Friday morning, thirty or so rugby players with time on their hands, what happened next? Steady there, young reader; it was not just so simple as you might have thought. In England at that time Good Friday was treated as a Sunday for the purposes of the licensing laws. Consequently, we were aware that at home the pubs would not have opened till noon[45]. But good old boozy Ireland where, we had heard, there was a bar in nearly every shop; where you could even get a drink whilst waiting for your prescription in the chemist's - obviously, there would be no problem. "What? Not open yet? What!! Not at all!? You're joking! Can't be shut all day, surely ... ". Hoping the coach driver was having a little joke we wandered off but we couldn't find anywhere that was open. We even struggled to find anyone on the deserted streets to ask but when we did and inevitably received a question in reply to our question – "Would it be a drink you're after?" - we were incredulous when he confirmed the pubs would not be opening at all that day. Incredible! Some muttered. Some grumbled. Some questioned the sanity of the organising committee. Some still did not believe it and set off to explore. In Ireland? Surely it could not be?

Two of us, who were of the exploring persuasion, walked down a street of ordinary terraced houses. As we passed one, which had nothing external to suggest it was a house any different from the others, we saw a large mirror on an inside wall. Although the premises were unlit we could see two men in the mirror, drinking a black, frothy liquid out of large glasses. They appeared to be standing at a bar. We tried the door and found it locked. However, rugby players do not reserve the reputation of dimwits, especially where ale is concerned; very soon one of us had a stroke of genius and suggested

---

[45] *The law used to limit public houses to open between noon and 2pm and between 7pm and 10pm (some districts 10.30) on Sunday in England. The law was changed in 2005 to permit "all-day drinking" after fears that this might lead to greater alcohol consumption, general drunkenness, loutish behaviour and absenteeism had been proven completely unfounded.*

we went round the back. We found the door open and, not being angels, went in. We were welcomed as "boys" by the landlord – we were to remain boys for the whole of our stay in Ireland – and, having been served, got talking to the men we had seen in the mirror. They were both farmers, both already three sheets to the wind and both trying to out-brag each other about how many acres they had ploughed before breakfast. Despite lacking any experience of agricultural matters, we realised at once it was Guinness Book of Records stuff. As they argued other customers joined in and the noise level rose. Then someone would put his fingers to his lips and 'Shhh!' theatrically. And, surprisingly, everybody did for a minute or two. We supposed they didn't know they could be seen in the mirror from the street and we couldn't help laughing to ourselves as it all seemed wonderfully Irish. But we could not have met more friendly people and when it was time to go the landlord insisted on giving us pint glasses for the bottles we had bought to take out. It was only a tiny bar and the glasses must have cost more than the small profit he had made out of us. When we returned to the coach we found we were the only ones to have found somewhere to get a drink. We put down the remarks about our good fortune and parentage to pure envy.

The replacement bus got us as far as Enniskillen where we were forced to stop again, this time for a puncture. By now it was it was lunchtime. Three of us went into a cafe and ordered some chips. "We only have chips for our friends," was the po-faced response. After the warmth of our reception in Dungannon we were completely taken back but the divide continued to be invisible to us.

The cafe apart, there were no signs of life anywhere. It would not have been a surprise if tumbleweed had rolled down the main street; the pubs definitely did not open in Enniskillen on Good Friday. But we had learnt from Dungannon not to despair. Eventually, we spotted three men leaning against a high stone wall; they were neither talking to each other nor doing anything which might attract attention. After a while one man went a few yards up the street, opened a door in the wall and went in. We noticed that further up the street, where the wall ended, what looked like it might be a pub began. We continued to watch the two remaining men with growing interest. They were joined, without any acknowledgement, by two more men. After an interval of a couple of minutes the two men who had been there first disappeared through the hole in the wall. The three of us went to lean against the wall. Not a word was spoken by the two remaining men but after a short while these two also went through the door. We waited for what we considered to be the appropriate interval before passing through the door and we found ourselves in the yard of what were obviously, from the stacks of crates of empty bottles, licensed premises. We went straight in through the back door. The third member of our party had not been with us when we found the pub at Dungannon and, despite the fact that we had brought bottles of beer and glasses back to the coach with us, he had remained doggedly sceptical. We had done a deal with him, namely, that if we, the experienced scouts, found a pub that was open he would buy the beer. It now appeared he was even doubting the evidence of his own eyes for although the bar was well populated with men wasting no time in getting on the right side of their pints he hesitated. But we were not going to give him chance to wriggle out of the deal and shoved him to the bar. Everyone in the place, including the barmaid, was looking at us by then for what we were: strangers. Our friend, who had not experienced the warmth of the welcome at Dungannon but still had the recent, unsettling incident of the chips on his mind was flustered and began with what seemed an unnecessary enquiry:

"Are you open?"

Without any hesitation the barmaid bluntly replied, "No," and maintained a deadpan which a professional gambler could not have bettered. Confused, the new member of the group turned away from the bar and back to us with a puzzled look of defeat on his face but we were not to be denied and told him,

"Never mind whether they're open or not. Get them in!"

He turned back to the barmaid and asked with all the assurance of a neutered mouse, "Can I have three pints, please?"

"Sure you can," she replied. "Why didn't you say before?"

We only had time for one quick one as we had to get back for the time set for the departure of the bus. However, when we got back to the car park no one had arrived to repair the puncture and there was a crowd of dry and disgruntled tourists who were becoming impatient.

Soon the queue by the hole in the wall probably exceeded by a considerable margin that which was not considered noticeable locally and the intervals between new entrants were also likely to have been less than the protocol demanded but it was not long before the entire touring party was in the pub. We were made very welcome by the locals who were very keen to discover what we, boys, were doing and, on being informed, they were pleased to find that it was something to which they could give their whole-hearted approval. The beer flowed and the noise level rose. It was not long before the tourists reached the point of not caring what was happening to the bus and the locals reached the point of not caring about the noise issuing from licensed premises which were closed on Good Friday. We gave them a few songs, somebody got going on the piano and they reciprocated with some good old Irish favourites. Later in the afternoon, the bus driver, having realised there was no danger of the mountain leaving its newly discovered hospitable environment any time soon, drew up outside the pub. I have an abiding memory of the entire pub's company, serving staff and all, coming out to see us off; they were still singing, cheering and waving on the pavement as we drew away. It was heart-breaking sixteen years later to hear the news that, in one of the worst atrocities of The Troubles, the Provisional I.R.A. had exploded a bomb during a Remembrance Day service in Enniskillen killing eleven people and injuring at least 63 others, nine of them seriously. It was difficult to suppose that there were many of those whose company we enjoyed on that day who were not in some way affected.

We had to stop at the border on our way to Sligo. It was sobering to see the border guards toting sub-machine guns. Although we were soon waved through we were still running late for our early evening kick-off. We need not have worried; it was another hour after our arrival before our hosts began to turn up in dribs and drabs. Sligo had a good pitch and a decent clubhouse. They had attractive, new-looking shirts with numbers on. They were not a bad side but we played well to gain a reasonably comfortable win. We could not stay as long as we would have liked with our hosts after the game as our bus driver was keen to get us to our destination in Ballina and get back home. For our part we were not sorry to contemplate the end of our brief association with Ulster Buses.

We rolled into Ballina and up to The Moy Hotel which stood on the banks of the river for which it was named. It was an unimpressive building which had seen better days. We poured in to be greeted not only by the landlord and landlady but also by a deputation from Ballina Rugby Club who apologised sincerely for having been unable to await our arrival before taking a drink but they pointed out we were, after all, a couple of hours late. It was another warm welcome and those Irish lads could certainly drink. The Vale, of course, responded to the challenge and were by no means disgraced. If anyone was worried about the possible effects on their performance the following day they kept it well disguised. "When in Rome ..." was probably the watchword on everyone's lips.

During the course of this reception we received a surprise addition to our touring party. One of the younger members at the club, who had been really looking forward to his first tour, had been denied the time off work at the last minute. However, being sent on a delivery near to Liverpool that day had proved too much of a temptation and he had got on the ferry in his employer's Transit van and driven himself to Ballina in it. This show of initiative failed by a large margin to impress the employer who somehow managed to get a phone call through to the new tourist at the hotel during which he was informed that due to his fine disregard for the rules of his employment he had joined the ranks of the unemployed. Not only that but he was going to be prosecuted for theft of the van and any other offence the former, rather irate employer could think of. Fortunately, solicitors do sometimes come in useful and, as I may have already mentioned we were not short of them amongst the playing members at The Vale.

One intervened to give the employer the benefit of certain observations, free of charge: first that Southern Ireland was out of the English jurisdiction and the alleged incident would not be of interest to the Gardaí and second it that if the owner's consent to drive the vehicle were to be withdrawn from the new tourist he would be unable to return the van to his employer but would be obliged to leave it on the west coast of Ireland and third provided the employee returned the keys to the employer that would counter the accusation of theft. The employer was greatly appreciative of the advice which was, after all, given free and which, he was not slow to realise, had had the beneficial effect of dissuading him from taking hasty steps which were not in his best interests; it put him in an altogether better humour and more forgiving frame of mind and it was consequently agreed that if the van and the keys were returned in one piece nothing further would be said. The new tourist was thus relieved of any anxiety which might have diminished his enjoyment of the tour; the loss of the job was accepted as a price worth paying.

That Saturday afternoon we played our hosts, Ballina. As we arrived at the ground were pleased to note that our drinking companions of the previous evening looked in no better state than we felt but we were taken aback when they informed us they were looking forward to watching a good game. The changing facilities were a shed at the back of a pub. The pitch had a hollow in the middle of it and the goalposts were slightly crooked. Ballina were the first to score. It was a typical tour game in that it was played in good spirit but it was not a great game from the point of view of rugby skills on display. The Vale struggled to impose any authority. Despite having the majority of possession and territory our finishing was less than clinical. We didn't have just the same snap we had had the previous evening. The match was drawing to a close with The Vale 3-0 down and, despite continuing to exert pressure, not really looking any more likely to score than we had the whole game. Another Vale attack petered out on their twenty five and there was a scrum. As the two packs engaged for the put-in, completely out of the blue, there was a loud shout from somewhere inside their eight of,

"Up the I.R.A. !"

Equally astonishing to us was the referee's immediate reaction: he gave a loud blast on his whistle and with his arm outstretched in our direction declared, in a heavy Irish accent,

"Ungentlemanly conduct. Penalty to The Vale."

The penalty award was accepted without demur by Ballina who mostly seemed as surprised as we were. It would have been churlish to decline such a gift even if the circumstances were bizarre and so we duly kicked the penalty to tie up the final score.

It was a good job we did not allow ourselves time that evening to reflect on this strange finish to the game otherwise we might have ended up seriously baffled instead of getting on with our touring.

Sunshine, moonshine and Guinness

The curious ending to the game had no adverse effect on the subsequent proceedings. We were royally welcomed and entertained by Ballina - the real players this time - that evening at the pub which hosted the changing facilities. In honour of our visit The Walsh Quartet had been hired to play. There were printed posters all round the pub and, indeed, all round the town, advertising the event. For the inhabitants of Ballina and for many miles around it was the only place to be that night. I will not bore the reader with an account of the evening's progress as it followed the general pattern of many a night on many a tour. That is not to say there were not incidents which The Vale tourists found highly amusing at the time and the memory of which still brings a smile but the sober tones of black and white read in the cold light of day would fail to do them justice.

I will just mention, however, that the playing of The Walsh Quartet was a revelation. It was not dance music as the tourists knew it and it certainly was not disco music. Even so there was no excuse for several of the party rolling up their trouser legs and donning handkerchiefs knotted in four corners before attempting to dance a jig. It looked like a cross between a Morris Dance and Knees Up Mother Brown but, fortunately, it was well received by the locals and accepted as all part of the hooley. There was more singing, dancing and . . . er . . . more beer, would you believe? Fortunately for them no other guests had been inspired to choose The Moy Hotel for a quiet Easter vacation for, after walking back there from the pub, we convinced ourselves that we were badly in need of a nightcap and poor Pascal, the landlord was roused to provide service; we were concerned that his stamina was already looking questionable.

Sunday was a rest day: a rest from rugby that is. On a short tour with a large squad the wisdom of having a rest day may be open to doubt. Those tourists who had already played twice thought it unlikely their services would be required a third time. This may have been a factor in the down-hill momentum which began to develop. Another factor was that there was nothing to do. The day started quietly enough; there was a sufficient number nursing headaches and hangovers to keep breakfast a subdued affair. The huge procession of vehicles in various states of disrepair, delivering worshippers to the nearby cathedral, provided a temporary diversion, convincing us there was then no equivalent of the MOT in Ireland. Then a walk seemed a good idea. It was a beautiful day. Contrary to expectations, given Ireland's reputation, we enjoyed warm, sunny weather with hardly a cloud in the sky, let alone a drop of rain for the whole tour. There's nothing like a sunny morning to lift the spirits.

It did not take us long to conclude our sightseeing tour of Ballina. I believe it is now a tourist honey-pot but at that time its attractions were limited, especially on an Easter Sunday. In the circumstances the lads from The Vale made a bold and original decision: to go back to the hotel and persuade Pascal to open the bar. There seemed to be a good number of locals in whose company we had been the previous evening who had had an inkling that this might happen. It wasn't long before the place was full and the hooley was picking up from where it had left off the night before. Pascal was alternately pleased by the merry ringing of the till and worried by the thought that it was not all within the bounds of the local licensing laws, the problem, seemingly, being that the non-residents should not have been there. However, it would be fair to say that The Vale lads neglected to give that problem a great deal of consideration at the time; in fact, they did not let it worry them at all until Pascal announced he was closing. Fortunately, he was a pliable fellow and his wallet found it difficult to refuse requests for just one more. Finally, I think only because he was exhausted, he did close the bar so he could have a rest but by this time the place was out of control; poor old Pascal had no idea what was going on or where.

It seemed a good idea to several of us to take advantage of the temporary bar closure to freshen up before the evening session but as we were passing a lounge by the top of the stairs on our way to our rooms we heard voices coming from the room although it was in darkness. Fresh from our experiences in Dungannon and Enniskillen we went in and sat down. We did not have long to wait before we were passed a bottle: it was either poteen, moonshine, mountain dew or Irish absinthe or all four for all we knew. It was remiss of us not to make appropriate enquiries as to the details. It was fiery stuff and very strong. It quite probably contributed to an incident which took place in the early hours: as the landlady was going down the corridor she passed a bathroom and noticed a flow of water coming from under the door. Fearing someone had left a tap running she opened the door to find, standing directly behind the source of the leak, a front row forward who was wearing only his customary silly grin; he had completely failed to notice that the toilet had been moved to the other side of the room since the last time he had been in there.

Team selection had to be revised the following morning to take account of the previous day and evening's events but a XV was put together which appeared capable of taking the field. We bid a fond farewell to The Moy Hotel and to Ballina and boarded the coach for Westport. On arrival The Vale selection was pleased to note that the pitch was not large. However, it did not appear to have had the lines marked out for a few months and whoever had done it had clearly not been sober at the time. The changing facilities needed only a few improvements to become basic. The opposition turned out in a motley collection of ragged old shirts; their numbers were made up by several players from another touring party who had not bothered to go home. We lost 20-0. It was embarrassing watching from the touchline. Not that I thought I could have done any better. We might have broken our duck from a penalty when someone shouted, "Up the I.R.A !" in a scrum but the referee didn't give it. We suspected he was an I.R.A. sympathiser but it was possible he might have been able to tell an English accent when he heard one.

We could not linger at Westport after the game as we had to get to Dublin to catch the ferry to Liverpool and we were going to make a detour to pick up the rope ladder specialist who had been refereeing somewhere further south. But, alas, it transpired that coaches in Southern Ireland were just as susceptible to punctures as buses in the North and they were no better equipped to deal with them. When the spare tyre finally did arrive the jack was inadequate and in the end we had to lift the back end of the coach ourselves. The end result was that we missed the ferry. Although we did not object to the prospect of a night out in Dublin we no longer had the funds available to do it justice.

Somehow our elder statesmen managed to find and to finance accommodation for the rest of us in Dublin that night. I don't know how they did it, I didn't bother to ask and I am sure I was not alone in failing to sufficiently express gratitude. The only excuse I can offer is that I was young. It is one of the strengths of club rugby that we do have more the mature players in our midst who are able to resolve such problems.

What do thirty, mostly broke, rugby players do when they find themselves with a day to spare in Dublin? They go round the Guinness brewery, of course, but it is a very big brewery and a very long way to walk before you get to the sampling room. The bar there was staffed by two men one of whom looked like he had been a second row in his day and, judging by his nose, had been a sucker for a right cross. He noted our blazers and opened the conversation, as the Irish generally seemed to like to do, with an easy question:

"Have you been playing rugby then, boys?"

"Yes. We've been on tour."

"And who might you have been playing, boys?"

"We played the first match against Sligo and ...""

"Sligo! That was my old club. Well, you'd get a good stuffing there, boys, I'm sure!"

We were perhaps not looking at our best but as my father often said: you can't judge a sausage by looking at its skin.

"No. We won at Sligo."

"Did you now, boys!" exclaimed our host, regarding the blow-ins before him with new-found respect mixed with disbelief.

"And who else did you play, boys?"

"Ballina."

"Ballina! You didn't play them, did you boys? If you beat Sligo you must have given them a real good hiding," chuckled our interrogator.

"We didn't play so well that day. We drew. Three all."

His smile disappeared and we could see the respect he had only very recently discovered had begun to diminish whilst the original disbelief was returning with a vengeance.

"Who else did you play, boys?"

As the lads at The Vale had no experience at telling untruths, there was a fatal delay and the opportunity to bring the playing side of the tour to an end after the Ballina game – which would not have been a long way from the truth - was lost.

"Westport."

"Westport!" The former Sligo lock shook with laughter. "Westport! Well, you must have had a field day there, boys."

Now, strictly speaking, this might have been regarded as a statement or as one of those rhetorical questions we have heard about earlier and those more experienced at not getting their webs tangled might have been able to quickly move the conversation along to a more beneficial topic. But the lads from The Vale were not versed in such dark arts and in the hiatus that ensued George Washington quietly admitted we had lost 20 nil. There was a sudden transformation; the barman's complexion took on the colour of an angry beetroot and he roared,

"You beat Sligo but you lost to Westport!" in a voice that must have been heard the other side of the Liffey.

And thus it came to pass that another first was added to The Vale's impressive list of touring honours: we were the first rugby club to be thrown out of the Guinness Brewery.[46]

The Vale tour of Ireland took place at Easter 1971. In the next Five Nations Tournament, because of the worsening security situation, both Scotland and Wales cried off from their matches against Ireland which were to have been held in Dublin. This was a huge disappointment for the Irish national team (which actually represented then, as it does now, the whole of Ireland, differing in that respect from most other sports). England and France had already been beaten away that year and there were great hopes of only a second Grand Slam to go with the first which was won in 1948. The following year the England team received a five minute standing ovation as they went on to the pitch at Lansdowne Road and John Pullin, the England captain, after losing the match 18-9, made the famous remark in his after-dinner speech: "We may not be much good but at least we turn up."

The triallist, the beer and the wardrobe

Just as it would be impossible to write about the mere mortals without including a tale about a tour, sadly, it would not be possible to avoid mentioning an altogether less savoury aspect of the social side of the game. In the previous tale I alluded to the incident of the hooker fly-pissing against a door and whilst I stand to be accused of exhibiting the soiled apparel I feel this is something which requires more than just a passing comment. It is a form of malfunction which occurs as more or less standard, not just on tour, but whenever beer is drunk to excess and the sleeping arrangements are unfamiliar. Everybody knows somebody who has been pisoriented at one time or another and they will divulge joyfully all the gruesome details of that person's misdeed even if they are much more reticent about similar aberrations of their own; it is nothing to brag about and yet there is a strange ambivalence about the thing. I really do not know why we find these often cringeworthy incidents funny and I do not want to know. But I suppose all jokes have to be at somebody's expense. It's one of those things like schadenfreude which belongs to the darker side of human nature. Something you are not quite comfortable with but find it difficult to avoid laughing at. Moreover, psychoanalysing piss-artistry is like dissecting a favourite poem word by word: the parts amount to so much less than the whole and by the time you've got the thing in bits the humour that was the gel has dissolved. But it must be said there is only any humorous content in the first place as long as it is not your stuff that gets peed on.

All tales of pisorientation share common factors. They revolve around someone going to bed seriously intoxicated, being only partially aroused from a deep alcohol-induced slumber by painful pressure on the bladder and being unable to locate the toilet. Often the perpetrator, if sharing a room, will awaken the other occupants by the noise he makes staggering around trying to discover where the toilet has been hidden - he knows it must be in there somewhere. For example, drawers may be opened in the quest, even quite small ones which would not normally be considered to have the capacity to provide an adequate hiding place for the toilet bowl. Wardrobes, however, are always the favourite place to begin the search; the sound of the doors being opened and hangers being moved in the desperate search for the relief giving receptacle tend to set the alarm ringing for the other occupants. The standard procedure when wakened in this situation is for them to maintain a watching brief but to shout loudly if there is a threat to their own belongings. The somnambulist will, of course, be allowed to pee on his own stuff and may, in fact, be encouraged heartily to do so.

It is not uncommon for the pisoriented person to leave the room in order to look for the toilet and he may continue his quest either in an adjacent room or further down the corridor as he follows the route imprinted on his subconscious to where his own domestic convenience would normally be. If this happens, once he has gone the other occupants, if they have been wakened, may react either by going back to sleep immediately or by locking the door (or by placing a chair underneath the handle should there be no lock) to prevent the danger returning. Should the phantom pisser be successful in finding a toilet of some description in another room his visit may go unnoticed until the following morning. When the evidence of a nocturnal accident is discovered initial suspicion inevitably falls upon the other occupants of that room.

"Which of you dirty bastards has pissed in the wardrobe?" shouts the victim whilst the others fall about laughing as they witness the damage to someone else's belongings. Needless to say, should an extra sleeping guest then be found in the room he will become the prime suspect.

It is not always the wardrobe; despite his semi-comatose condition the sprinkler can be quite imaginative in his choice of receptacle although his judgment of capacity may well have been seriously impaired. Thus plant pots and ornaments such as small jugs may be mistaken for the real thing and shoes also come high on the list. (The seasoned tourist always ensures his shoes and bag are not left on the floor or in the bottom of the wardrobe and will usually be observed to stow them well away under his own bed, failing a more secure location. However, such is the ingenuity of the pisoriented drunkard that nowhere is guaranteed to be completely safe).

A typical example of this semi-conscious improvisation concerns a player from The Vale who was selected for a County trial match. This was a huge honour for a member of a junior club especially one who had never played rugby until early adulthood when he fell victim to a pioneering use of child psychology by The Vale's recruiting officer: "What's a big, useful lad like you doing not playing rugby?" (I don't want to give too many details in case someone is able to identify him and I would hate that to happen as he has refused to pay the very reasonable appearance fee I suggested).

The trial was held at the ground of one of the county's senior clubs and after the game new friendships were formed in the traditional manner. A night on the town followed, the Vale lad having previously been offered a berth at the parental home of one of the triallists from the senior club hosting the trial. The honour of selection was celebrated well rather than wisely and the Vale lad woke the following morning with a thick head. Despite that handicap he noticed that the atmosphere at breakfast was rather cooler than it had been the previous evening. As soon as he was able to catch his new friend alone, already fearing he may have unwittingly committed some misdemeanour, he asked him if anything was the matter.

"John," said his friend (everyone at The Vale at that time - apart from the Welsh scrum-half - was called John), "do you remember what you did last night?"

It was the question every excessive reveller dreads.

"In parts," replied John, suddenly filled with foreboding.

"Do you remember going into my aunt's bedroom and turning the light on?"

"Er. No. I'm afraid I don't actually remember that bit at all."

"You were stark, bollock-naked at the time."

"Oh dear! I wasn't , was I ?"

"You went towards the bed. Although my aunt shouted at you, you carried on towards her and ..."

"Oh dear me! No! I didn't, did I?"

". . . you lifted the lid of the bedding box at the foot of the bed and pissed in it."

"Oh !Hell! I'm really sorry and ..."

"But then, to cap it all, John, you left the lid up afterwards!"

There was no more to be said. He synchronised his apologies with his farewells and left immediately.

Up the Poles

Fund-raising at The Vale was a more or less permanent activity in the era spanned by these tales. No doubt it would be described nowadays as part of a "policy of continuous improvement" but it was not a policy which had been formally adopted at the club; at that time it just seemed the natural thing to do in order to benefit current and future generations. There was an army of willing helpers led by a dedicated committee; everyone was expected to do their bit and that meant helping with the organisation, selling tickets and attending money-raising functions. Certain stalwarts always stood out but, with few exceptions, the membership made a full contribution. Every Christmas much effort was put into a big raffle which offered a very worthwhile cash prize as well as "star" prizes bought from local stores at a big discount in return for some advertising. There was also a long list of other prizes donated by members which made the total number up to a hundred. Traditionally, the last prize to be drawn was a "shorty, kinky, see-through nightie". When it made its debut it had been considered a bit risqué and it never failed to draw a laugh even in later years, still more so if the identity of the winner was known. It often was as many members ended up buying the tickets they had been allotted to sell. Needless to say, if the winner was a lady present there would be a numerous requests for an impromptu modelling. All good, clean fun - comparatively speaking.

The talents of the Ladies Committee went far beyond providing match teas; under the direction of the former captain, who was to blame for bringing me into the game, they catered for a number of events each year which were always a sell-out and at which, as usual, the bar did very well. All these events sold themselves on merit; they were good value for money. The organisation, the labour involved in the preparation and in the cleaning-up and washing-up afterwards were provided free of charge by the Ladies Committee and other club members, particularly the Entertainments Committee. The amount of work which went in was truly remarkable and it was a privilege to be associated with such a dynamic and dedicated bunch of volunteers who had their sights so firmly set on going forward.

The considerable proceeds from all these efforts were mainly invested in improving the club's facilities but also in keeping the playing members' annual subscriptions and match fees down. These were, in fact, extremely modest for what the players got in return. Nevertheless, the principle was that you paid to play. That made it your club and you shared responsibility for it. Rather than moan about any lack of facilities or any other problem, you would be told in no uncertain terms, "If you don't like it get up off your backside and do something about it! It's your club."

This attitude helped to keep morale high. Many other sports clubs in the area were "works" teams where whatever was provided was provided by the employer and whatever was provided was never quite enough; the more people had it put on a plate for them the pickier they seemed to get. Much always seemed to want more if the responsibility for the provision of the more lay elsewhere. The sense of having a personal interest in the club also had a strong effect on loyalty. It was rare for a player to leave The Vale to join another club unless he was either leaving the area or had decided, usually with the full encouragement of his team-mates, to try his luck at a higher standard with a more senior club. In that case the door would always be open if he wanted to come back.

In due course, sufficient money was raised to embark on a big programme of improvements. Farmer Dinsdale was persuaded to part with some more land so that a new pitch could be created and at the same time the existing one was improved. The proposal to install new drainage did, of course, cause an environmental outcry and it was a relief to discover that the existing pitch had never been officially registered as a wetland. Fortunately, because they had been obliged by the activities of the warden to keep a low profile, nobody outside the club knew about the hippos or we would never have got away with it. Even so a disproportionate part of the improvement expenses was down to the cost of transporting them to a new home: in the dead of night a fleet of special, unmarked trucks sped them off to Colbourne where they lived almost as happily ever after.

The clubhouse was extended to provide a new lounge with quality carpets and soft furnishings and even a television. The bar itself was, of course, also extended. It was all very plush. Everyone was very proud, particularly the older hands who could remember the rudimentary facilities associated with earlier pitches The Vale had called home. Prior even to the hut with the copper boilers being provided by The Corporation on The Prairie, there were several who could remember a changing room in a loft at a nearby pub from which the players descended naked to the washing facilities by means of a trap door in the floor and a ladder fixed to the wall. To quote a contemporary, "The sight from below beggared description." The transformation had been achieved over the span of a generation. The Vale's wanderings around the valley were over.

As a consequence of all these improvements The Vale had a set-up equalled by very few local junior clubs at that time. Combined with a long-standing reputation for hospitality which was enhanced by the excellence of the Ladies Committee's catering it became attractive for other clubs to play there and the fixture secretary worked assiduously at obtaining new fixtures. This led to The Vale receiving the honour of playing the first match on English soil against a Polish team. They were from a place no-one had heard of at the time called Gdansk[47].

With the honour of hosting the first game of their tour went the obligation of accommodating the Polish party. They could not afford to pay for hotel accommodation and so the players and whatever the Polish equivalent of alickadoos may be, were billeted amongst The Vale membership. The Poles arrived one Friday

---

[47] *The name Danzig might have been more familiar; that was the German name for the city, it having been part of Germany until the end of The Second World War. It was before Lech Walesa and the Solidarity movement began the chain of events which made the name of Gdansk famous.*

afternoon in November at the Vale clubhouse where a reception was held to welcome and feed them and introduce them to their individual hosts. Very soon after their arrival the first problem was discovered: none of them could speak English. This was entirely fair given that no-one from The Vale could speak Polish but, needless to say, the lack of linguistic skills on the part of the visitors was totally unexpected whilst our own inadequacy in that direction was taken for granted. Nevertheless, the welcoming speech was received well. In fact, it was received well before it should have ended. Not long after he had begun, the speaker, having considered himself to have made a weighty remark, paused slightly for emphasis and a Vale player found himself attuned to such a degree with the point being made that he was moved to put his hands together. This, in turn, motivated the entire Polish contingent to do likewise so enthusiastically and at such length that the speaker was eventually obliged to dismiss any thought of a meaningful resumption. With good grace he gave it up and signalled it was time to retire to the bar.

By means of lists of names, nods, shakes and mimes guests were introduced to hosts and there was soon a throng around the bar intent on cementing these new acquaintances in the manner guaranteed to transcend cultural boundaries. The Vale players, of course, stood the first round and the Poles quickly learnt "Cheers" and the English "Nazdrovia". It hardly needs to be mentioned that further conversational progress proved difficult in view of the linguistic limitations of both sides. When things got really sticky, to break an awkward silence "Cheers" or "Nazdrovia" were frequently resorted to in order to keep the pot boiling. Consequently, the first pints disappeared even faster than usual, the Poles seeming to have taken to English ale with a minimal need to adjust their palates. However, it is difficult enough to maintain a conversation with just one word and a single theatrical prop but when both word and prop become simultaneously redundant it becomes impossible. There are only so many times you can put that empty glass down on the bar and pick it up again to examine it in order to satisfy yourself that it has not yet somehow miraculously refilled itself, before replacing it on the bar and resuming the silence.

"Would you like another?" is very easily rendered in sign language and so The Vale lads stood another round. Then another. It became obvious that the guests' new-found taste for English ale was unmatched by their willingness to pay for it. The reason, discovered later, was not just that they did not have any money for hotel accommodation but that they did not have any cash at all. The currency regulations in the Eastern bloc then in force neither allowed them to exchange any of their money for pounds in Poland nor to take any of their own currency out of their country. Suddenly the price of ale had been doubled. That was a seismic event very high on the Richter scale. Chancellors of the Exchequer had been known to add a penny or two to the price of a pint on Budget Day and decimalisation[48] had recently given brewers and landlords an excuse to round up their profit margins but this was as serious as it was sudden; as near to a man-made disaster as might occur in our green and pleasant land. Picture the scene; it was late Friday afternoon; in their pockets the Vale lads had either such cash as they could afford to spend or such cash as they had thought would last them over the weekend; the banks did not open on Saturday morning at that time[49] and there were no cash machines[50]. Fortunately, despite the lack also of cheque guarantee cards at that time, the steward would cash a cheque for a reasonable amount so that at least those who had bank accounts were able to have access to some more cash. By means of some teeming and ladling based on short term loans between the hads

---

[48] *Decimalisation took place on 15 February 1971*

[49] *When these Tales began they used to open, as they do now, but there was a spell which started in the 70s when trade union power caused them to be closed.*

[50] *Barclays Bank in Enfield Town North London was the first to install a forerunner of the cash or automated teller machine on 27 June 1967 but these did come into widespread use for another decade.*

and the had-nots – "Well, all right, but you'd better pay me back next week." - liquidity was restored.

As the evening progressed it became noticeable that four of the touring party did not quite seem to fit in with the others; they kept mostly to themselves. One was a lady and the other three looked too old to play for one thing but for another they stood out by being better dressed than the rest. It turned out their real party was the Communist Party; they were the local members of the Politburo. They had no connection with the rugby club or with rugby at all. They were there as minders to see that the players toed the party line during their visit whilst they enjoyed a freebie. (Politicians, then as now, were politicians the world over). The authority for what could and what couldn't be done lay with them and not the team captain. The point was emphasised at 10pm when the leader of the gang of four apparently told the players to stop drinking; they were to leave, go to where they were staying and go to bed as they would be playing the following day. Their captain protested but only weakly and briefly and with some muttering the players left.

The leader of the gang of four was billeted with me. He was in no mood to call it a night as far as he, personally, was concerned. I didn't speak any Polish and he didn't speak any English but we discovered we both spoke a little German so we were able to communicate after a fashion. We ended up at one of the local fleshpots where he soon decided that a Pernod on ice chased by a half of Guinness knocked spots of a shot of vodka followed by a glass of lager and he demonstrated his political skills fully by getting his neck round as much as he possibly could at someone else's expense. My only consolation was that I enjoyed a truly cosmopolitan evening - a Pole and an Englishman communicating in German in a club with a Spanish name, drinking alternately French and Irish beverages – or so I tried to persuade myself as I cashed another cheque at the club the next day.

My guest didn't manage to get up too early the following morning for which other members of the touring party were grateful. They had managed to persuade their hosts –somebody had by then been found to interpret – to take them to the local market where they had a field day in the absence of their minders. They bought fents of cloth to take back with them to make into clothes either for themselves or to sell. They did have some money with them after all, if not a lot, but it was black money and they dared not let any of the gang of four know about it. We understood the situation. They all seemed genuine enough, a decent set of lads, and we were more inclined to feel sorry for them rather than begrudge them their purchases and any profit they could make.

The warmth of these sentiments was not reciprocated on the field. In true English fashion The Vale won the forward battle but could not get the corresponding number of points on the board. Nevertheless, they were leading and pressing for the clinching score as full time approached but then the Poles ran the ball from behind their own try-line "like a load of bloody March hares" as one Vale supporter put it or as The Sunday Times reported, "in a gesture of "magnificent optimism". The Polish equivalent of Blanco, Hancock and Obolensky all combined to make the score which resulted in The Vale having the honour of being the first English team to lose to a Polish one on English soil. However, according to The Sunday Times, "The real hero of the match was the referee. Speaking no Polish, he invented a complete language of his own and drove his meaning home with wild gesticulations, grunts, snarls and home-made phrases such as 'footsky upsky'. "

To add insult to injury The Vale players were obliged to assist their guests in the celebration of their victory to an extent beyond the call of duty but by then they had just got used to getting their hands down. However, they were not sorry to be relieved of that unexpected part of their obligations as hosts when the guests were delivered to another club the following day for the second match of their tour. Despite vociferous support from The Vale, for some reason Gdansk were unable to reproduce the magic they had displayed the previous day and the home side ran out comfortable winners.

For once, The Vale were outshone not just on the field but also by the lengths to which the home side had gone to welcome the visitors. There was a reception after the match which was not, in itself any more lavish than that which had been provided at The Vale, of course, but the attendance of a party of civic dignitaries in their official regalia who were accompanied by a proper interpreter took their reception to a higher level of pomp and ceremony. As mentioned earlier one of the gang of four was a lady, an apparatchik, I suppose. However, she gave more of an impression than her three comrades that, besides fulfilling her official duties she was there to enjoy herself. She seemed to be the link between the players and the management and she was more familiar with the players than the other three. So much more familiar, in fact, that it caused some curiosity amongst the Vale lads who, of course, were keen to learn anything they could about politico-cultural aspects of a foreign country. They wondered whether she had some kind of a dual role and attempts were made to establish the exact nature of her status. However, they came up against the language barrier: one of the Polish lads did a kind of mime using his hands and feet whilst the others fell about laughing but no-one was able to understand what riding a bicycle had to do with politics.

She was a strapping lass, approaching a certain age who might best be described as on the healthy side of handsome and quite lively. Now whether his interest lay in seeking tips as to how to go about establishing a Politburo in the town or whether it lay in another direction is uncertain but one of the civic party was very keen to pursue a conversation with her. The official interpreter was engaged elsewhere but as it turned out that the lady in question also spoke German I was roped in to assist. Although it was obvious that she spoke the language a lot better than me I just about managed to keep the conversation going. They say that confidence and not being frightened of making mistakes are the keys to speaking foreign languages; a couple of beers helps with both these requirements and soon words I had learnt at school but since forgotten seemed to be returning in an encouraging fashion. The conversation started well and the body language suggested that the lady was flattered by the interest taken by the dignitary. In fact, it seemed to me that she had taken quite a shine to him; perhaps, being an apparatchik, she was impressed by the length of his gold chain. It was all small talk to start with but then the conversation began to take on a more personal nature and I got the impression he was trying to chat her up. In fact, despite him having the appearance of a stuffed shirt, had I known anything about those things I would have said he was doing pretty well at it as she was giggling a lot. He had been leading the dialogue by a series of nicely paced questions but then, suddenly, he dried up. There was a pause and he seemed to panic. In his eagerness to fill the vacuum, for the sake of something to say, he asked me to ask, "How many times has she been in England." This was really going right back to the beginning of the conversation and quite out of context but it wasn't my place to do anything other than translate so I put the question as requested. By way of reply the lady party member gave the dignitary a smack round the chops. In fairness, it was more playful than powerful and accompanied by a laugh and a naughty smile; a touch of Dick Emery's,

"Ooh ! You are awful - but I like you."[51]

From what I have learnt since I suspect there could be some rugby players (from other clubs, of course, not from The Vale, where we were all good, clean-living lads) who might have said to themselves, "Here's a girl with spirit. With some refinement to my approach I could be in here." However, if the dignitary had been harbouring any thoughts of a bit of slap and tickle it was definitely not the kind he had in mind and certainly not in so public a place; it did his dignity no good at all. I have never seen anyone look so stunned. He left the scene immediately without a further word but he gave a withering look to the amateur interpreter which was frosty enough to

---

[51] *Dick Emery starred in his own TV comedy series in the 60s and 70s and this was the catchphrase of his best known character, the brassy blonde, Mandy who played the title role in his full-length feature film in 1972*

have obliterated a whole bank of the hardiest snowdrops. Of course, I was just as gobsmacked as he was even if not literally. The lady herself looked a little disappointed by the abrupt ending to an exchange which had started so promisingly. I looked at my watch and realised that I could just about make it back to The Vale in time for last orders.

I remained completely baffled by the lady's reaction to what had seemed a completely innocent question until the following day when I was able to get hold of a German dictionary to look a few things up. Even then it was difficult to work it out but in the end I came to the conclusion that due to possible differences in pronunciation, neither of us being natural German speakers, the noise in the clubhouse, the question being out of context etc, etc ... well, not to put too fine a point on it, it seemed that instead of me asking the lady "how many times she had been in England" I had, unfortunately, asked her "how many times she had been had in England."

Missing Molars

In an earlier chapter I recalled a dark and dismal day in February and a game I played in the dales with The Vale. You got to hear about one of my famous rugby exploits when I kicked a goal. This time you get to hear about my other famous rugby exploit: when I scored my solo try. This time it was a lovely day; I could tell spring had arrived because I wouldn't have been able to count the blades of grass on the second team pitch without taking both socks off. There was no standing water to be seen anywhere. The crests of the little muddy hollows were turning to the prettiest shade of charcoal grey you ever saw as they dried out under the benign influence of a light but balmy breeze. On the distant blue horizon were some tiny, white clouds, looking as harmless as lost sheep. The sun had got his hat on and was playing with the breeze at making shadows under the old oak tree which stood by the clubhouse entrance. It was just the Saturday afternoon for a game of rugby. There was only one problem: I had been injured the previous week and was unable to play. It was nothing serious, just a dead leg. At first I hadn't accepted it when more experienced players told me I would be out for at least a week but when I could hardly walk on the Sunday and was not much better by Wednesday when my card came, I had decided to tell the team secretary I would not be available. Now the weather was rubbing it in by coming up with a glorious day. Typical! Nevertheless, I was not downhearted; I decided I would take the second best option to playing and go down to the club anyway; there I would enjoy a pint or two and then some fresh air whilst watching the game; I would shout encouragement alternately with good-natured abuse to work up a thirst and enjoy another pint or two with the lads afterwards: nothing too strenuous; it seemed an attractive programme for an afternoon's gentle relaxation. Awarding myself full marks for ingenuity, and filled with the joys generally inspired by the pleasantness of the day I waltzed into the clubhouse, with hardly a limp. Before I could pass a glass to my lips I was pounced upon by a lurking blue and yellow tiger in the form of the third team captain. They were short, desperately short, he said and pleaded with me to turn out for them. My unprepared objections appeared at first to receive consideration but he produced a telling argument: I could just as easily enjoy the fresh air standing on the wing as on the other side of the touchline; I wouldn't need to do anything, just be seen to be filling what would otherwise be a space. I thought about it and somehow the injury didn't seem as bad as it had at the beginning of the week – it was only a bit of a dead leg, after all, and I might be able to run it off. The third team skipper was a really good bloke who had helped me on my way in times past, the sun was shining and it seemed the noble thing to do, to turn out with the other lads and do my bit however insignificant, for the club in its hour of need. And I would say this to any young player who might find himself in a similar situation: make sure you do not go within a mile of the clubhouse until well after kick-off.

Thoughts of a beer now postponed I set off at full speed back home to collect my kit, feeling fitter by the minute. In the short time it took me to drive home and back I had convinced myself I was fit enough to play.

"Desperately short", the skipper had said. Ten minutes later I dashed back with my kit and found out how short "desperately short" was. As I entered the changing room, I raised my hand in mute apology for interrupting the skipper's team talk. To my surprise, he thanked me warmly. It turned out I had just volunteered to play scrum-half. So much for pleasantly taking the air on the wing! To be honest I didn't mind that much; I had never played that position before in a match so at least it would be a first and I was by now convinced I was fully fit. The adrenalin was beginning to flow and I was quite looking forward to being the first in line to get hands on all that lovely ball.

Inevitably, fairly soon into the game, there was a scrum. Their scrum-half put the ball in, they hooked it and their scrum-half went round to the back of their scrum to collect. I was standing, watching all this activity and wondering what I should be doing when all of a sudden the ball squirted out from between their second and back rows right at my feet. All I had to do was pick it up, canter the full length of at least ten yards and touch down for a try. All of which I duly accomplished with great panache. Nothing to it. I began to think I could get to like playing scrum-half. Not long afterwards, from a similar field position, now brimming with confidence and expecting to repeat my earlier success, I collected the ball from the base of our scrum and made a dart round the blindside where I found out why I was a bit tall for a scrum-half. I can't say whether it was a stiff arm, a swinging arm, a short arm or what it was because I never saw it coming but it was definitely an arm of some description.

On Monday morning I found myself in the waiting room of a dentist's surgery. As the clock crept towards 9.15 I reflected that this was not the ideal time to be in such a place. The dentist was a genial, young Irishman who, at that time had no claim to fame other than the fact that he lived a few doors away from me. On hearing of my plight, he had kindly offered to see me first thing Monday morning. On Saturday night in the club bar, after an abundant quantity of self-administered anaesthetic, it had seemed churlish to refuse this generosity on his part. But now I remembered that when a terrible thirst came upon my friend and neighbour, as it did frequently between Friday evening and Sunday night, the smile on the club Treasurer's face would broaden as any worries that we might not reach the brewery's monthly barrelage quota evaporated.

At last, I was ushered in to the surgery. However, not long after taking a seat my fears were realised for "the toot' could not be saved at all." What was left would have to come out and I would have to have a plate.

It was to be the beginning of a long love-hate relationship. I don't mean with the dentist. Anyone who can see the erotic potential in being strapped into a chair with your mouth wide open whilst a man with beery breath prepares to inflict pain on you would have been called, in less enlightened times, a pervert. No, of course, it was the plate and I who had the love-hate relationship. The thing I did like about the plate was that I could once again smile without having to try to keep my top lip down on the left side of my face to hide the gap in my teeth. When I did that it gave me a slightly sinister aspect which used to make the cat nervous. What I didn't like about it was that my mouth never really felt comfortable with the plate in, even after my tongue had finally got bored with exploring every nook and cranny and had reluctantly accepted the plate as a part of my mouth. I soon came to think of them as the ceremonial molars, to be worn on official duties only and took the plate out whenever I felt there was no necessity to keep up appearances. For its part, I think that the plate felt it deserved a permanent rather than a part-time position and it was annoyed when its services were so casually dispensed with. When I was in a relaxed mode I developed the habit of taking the plate out and slipping it in my trouser pocket. Little did I know the depth of resentment this caused or that the denture was plotting to exact a terrible revenge for being slighted in that way. One Saturday night as I returned home after a convivial evening at the club I had the misfortune to trip over the aforementioned cat as it fled from an over-exuberant smile. That gave the denture the chance it had long been waiting for. In the ensuing tumble, involving a collision with an armchair, it took advantage of the confusion to bite me sneakily but grievously in the groin. But I wasn't fooled; I knew who had done it.

It was an unfortunate ending to what had otherwise been an enjoyable evening. For the first time in a long time we had even done the three-man-lift (but you don't want to hear about that just now so I will save it till later). The whole company had coincided in their intent to make a night of it: nobody had had to leave early for other commitments and the opposition, with whom we generally had a good rapport, were on a coach and had stayed on. One of their players was getting married the following week so it was a kind of stag night and they were disposed to give it plenty from the start. It was also the last game at the club for one of our number who was going abroad. The Vale player was a popular lad and we were all keen to give him a good send-off. He was what was known as a utility forward: in other words he was a bit too tall and narrow for the front row, not quite tall enough for the second row and not quite quick or dirty enough for the back row. But he was an amiable lad, always tried his hardest and would play anywhere without complaining. He was also a good lad to have with you when it came to the après match activities. He could take his ale as well as the next man and never failed to stand his round. But the thing was that at bar games he was absolutely hopeless. He was extremely good-natured about it, always seemed to get a lot of fun out of it and never opted out although it cost him money week after week but hopeless nonetheless. At fizz-buzz he would fizz when he should have buzzed and buzz when he should have fizzed. At pass the bottle he would hang on when he should have passed and then pass when he should have hung on. On the field of play this would have been unremarkable since, week in, week out, that was how the majority of us played our rugby but at bar games there was the club's reputation to consider. Nevertheless, although he did not have a safe pair of hands, our friend – Jim, I'll call him – had his part to play.

That evening after the game we warmed up on a few swift halves gained at Jim's expense, at some minor sport whilst waiting for the main events. We sang *"We are the boys from down The Vale"* but we didn't sit on the floor on that occasion. Sometimes doing that might encourage ale-throwing which, apart from the fact that the price of ale was always going up, had become frowned upon because of regular improvements to the club's facilities. Also, I think, to be fair that we were becoming a bit more fashion conscious as the sixties decade progressed[52] and were more reluctant to put our light-coloured strides into contact with the floor. Or perhaps we were just starting to get soft. Whatever the reason, the problem was that whilst it was a good thing you no longer got your backside wet, to sing it standing up went against the actual words and it didn't seem quite right. I suppose

---

[52] *The younger reader might like to look up "Carnaby Street" on the internet and listen to The Kinks recording of "Dedicated Follower of Fashion".*

we should have substituted the line about sitting on the floor but tradition is tradition after all.

Having opened the choral section of the evening vigorously we politely called upon the opposition to reciprocate with a song of their own. For the uninitiated, the traditional invitation goes like this:-

> *"We call upon Harlequins to sing us a song,*
> *We call upon Harlequins to sing us a song,*
> *We call upon Harlequins to sing us a song*
> *So sing, sing or show us your ring!*
> *We don't want to see your ring*
> *So sing, you bastards, sing!"*

(It might not have been Harlequins we were playing: I just use the name as an example as it fits the metre).

It's normally a good formula to provoke a response and they replied with some commonplace rugby song. Nothing memorable; it was not a bad effort but it was clearly a moral victory to The Vale. We then sang a few songs together after which we moved on to bar games. It was all innocuous stuff to start with. A couple of their lads were taken in with Cockeroo but most of them were familiar with that one, having played The Vale over many seasons. There was talk from The Vale about the three-man-lift but it then it was decided that it was a bit too early for that yet; the suspense was all part of the build-up; perhaps later. There was plenty of banter and the beer was found to be in its usual good form. As the evening drew on the competitive streak began to return and both sides started to weigh up what game they thought they might be able to beat the opposition at. However, it didn't matter which game was selected in the end because, before any bets were placed, Jim would be hailed as The Vale's star performer, the potential match-winner. Yet in the warm-up runs it would become fairly obvious that Jim's co-ordination was a bit off, leading to a conversation along lines similar to the following:-

"Not on your usual form yet, Jim?"

"No. But I'll be all right when I've got my eye in after a couple more pints."

One of the Vale lads would then make an audible aside to one of the opposition, "Amazing the difference when he's pissed". Meanwhile Jim's reactions seemed to be getting worse with every sip.

Just before the game proper was due to start and the bets had been taken Jim would excuse himself on the pretext of letting a bit out so that the pressure on his bladder would not affect his concentration. He would not return and would defy all attempts to locate him. The Vale Games Captain would exhibit signs of increasing agitation, asking his lieutenants, "Where the hell can he be?" or "Go and see if he's gone for some fresh air outside somewhere." Finally, when the opposition were becoming restive (although, of course, sympathetic about the absence of Vale's star player) The Vale's Games Captain would be obliged to concede with a worried look, "All right, all right! I don't know what's happened to him but we're going to have to start without him," and turning to the rest of The Vale players, "Is there anyone who can stand in – it doesn't matter if you haven't played before?" And a narrow-eyed wing-forward would step up to take Jim's place.

Yes, it had been a splendid evening apart from the cat and the denture incident. If you play rugby you are never too young to wear dentures although, I am glad to say, nowadays a good gum-shield is not as difficult or costly to obtain as it once was and most players have the good sense to wear them. I didn't wear one before the incident as I knew it wouldn't happen to me. It may seem strange to the younger reader that we did not all always wear gum-shields but, at that time plastic ones were only just coming on the market and had a long way to go in their development; they were made out of a thick, fairly rigid plastic mould and one size supposedly fitted all. After attempting to trim the mould with scissors to something approaching the right size for your mouth, the mould had to be immersed in very hot water until pliable and then quickly transferred into your mouth and pushed vigorously on to your upper set whereupon you were supposed to bite hard and to hold it there until it cooled and took on the right shape. The thing was that if you did not have the water hot enough or you were not quick enough in getting it into position in your mouth, it came out again the same shape as it went in but if you did have the water hot enough you scalded your mouth. You had to get it right first time; once your mouth had been scalded you couldn't put the thing in again so you gritted your teeth and put up with the choking sensation as long as you could. Only when you were certain you had done it did you open your mouth and watch the wretched thing catapult across the room. The only other alternative was to get a proper rubber one made and that usually meant private treatment at the dentist's which was almost as dear relatively then as it is now.

There was also an element of machismo. At that time no self-respecting cricketer wore any protective headgear, not even amateur batsmen in the Lancashire League facing fearsome fast bowlers like the West Indies Test players, Wes Hall and Charlie Griffith; building workers didn't wear safety helmets if they could avoid it, let alone gloves or masks. Now, of course, the wearing of a helmet or gum-shield is a matter of course and building workers regularly pass round the moisturising cream at brew-time.

As dentures are generally associated with the older person I did not wish it to be generally known that my perfect smile was less than original. After the bite in the groin, not life changing but near enough to provide a solemn warning, I had to find places other than my trouser pocket in which to put my plate when I felt I could get away with not wearing it. However, a similar thing occurred to me then as it does now with reading glasses. Having come to need these in later life, the brain has not yet become fully trained to a proper management routine; I tend to put them down all over the place and then cannot find them. As a result I have had to buy several pairs. Nevertheless, I still often find myself without a pair and obliged to instigate a search of all the usual places. I will say this for reading glasses: they are gregarious creatures. When I do finally catch up with them, more often than not, I find two or more pairs in the same place.

How they manage this is another of life's little mysteries I have been unable to resolve. Of course, other people stop this habit of sneaking off that glasses have, by putting them on a chain and when I see someone with their glasses on a chain round their neck in public I am never sure whether to congratulate them on their practicality or lament their lack of style. But I digress. The point is, of course, that whether it is glasses or dentures, you need to cultivate the habit of always putting them back in the same place when you are not wearing them. If you do this you will save yourself from the irritation of being interrupted in your search by that stupid question: "where did you last have them?"

I used to manage all right with the plate when I could just put it in my trouser pocket but when that became out of bounds I struggled to re-organise myself. Consequently, my denture would sometimes go missing. The arrival of Monday morning would often be accompanied by a frantic search of jacket pockets and other possible hiding places. Of course, the Monday morning eventually arrived when it could not be found at all and I had to resign myself to setting off to work without it. For some reason, the folly of youth, no doubt, I believed the girls at work were unaware I wore a plate and I wished to save myself from the embarrassment of them finding out.

As the first in to the office that Monday morning I was greeted with a grin from the ceremonial molars who were sitting on top of a pile of papers on my desk. My joy at seeing them again was soon diluted when I began to wonder how they had got there. Then I remembered I had stayed on to finish something on Friday evening; I must have taken the plate out then after everyone had gone home. But I wouldn't have placed it so strategically, lord of all it surveyed, on top of the pile of papers, surely? If I had I would have noticed it before I left? Somebody must have put it there. But who? With some foreboding I went through the possibilities then with sudden relief I thought of the cleaner. Yes: that was it! She came in Friday evening. She must have found the plate somewhere and decided it was a worthy exhibit. Although this revelation did not cause me to mimic the sand boy at least I had got the denture back before the girls came and the damage was limited; I rarely saw the cleaner anyway and the denture had been fairly clean, not caked in food or anything. I could handle that. It could have been a lot worse. I'd had a lucky escape. But wait a minute: I remembered that there had been some fuss and bother a couple of weeks ago. The girls had said the cleaner was useless and she would have to go but instead of advertising for someone else they had got a rota up to do the cleaning themselves on Saturday mornings.

Bring on the Oranges: the Sunday Match

Do you remember the time when a touch kick hit the tray of oranges and scattered them all in the mud? Or the other time when that dozy donkey of a second row stumbled and spilt the whole tray as he was bringing it up to the pitch? It's a tricky business trying to dust them off. What about the time when someone forgot to bring the oranges and we had to make do with just two lemons snaffled from behind the bar and sliced up to go round both teams? Who was it who used to have a drink from the sponge bucket at half-time if it hadn't been used much? The dirty bugger. (Speaking of the constant need to drink water isn't it amazing we didn't have weekly deaths from dehydration?)

As you will have guessed the first half is over. I expect you could do with a breather. You've done well to make it so far. The Vale won the toss so it will be a bit easier in the second half: we'll be playing downhill with the wind behind us – it always blows from the south west and gets up a bit as the afternoon goes on – so we'll be able to keep them pinned down in the bottom corner. It's not too cold today and it's just stopped raining so we're not going to turn straight round and there's a little bit of time to fill in. I haven't got the technology to show action replays of the highlights in the first half even if there had been any so I'm going to have to think of something to keep your interest until play starts again.

You have already heard about the time I kicked a goal and the time I scored a try so that pretty well deals with the achievements of my playing career. All that remains is to tell you about what turned out to be the crowning glory of my time on the pitch although I didn't realise it at the time. Half-time marks in these tales marks the end of my playing part as one of the mere mortals; I shall not be turning out for the second half due to injury. I am sorry to depress you in this light-hearted look at rugby by introducing this moment of what, I am sure you will all agree, was a great sadness and loss, especially to me, but these things happen so please put your hankies away or you'll make your eyes all red. The injury was nothing horrendous, looked at objectively, but somehow, I managed to knacker one of my knees whilst playing rugby of all things. You did need knees after all: both of them; they had been fibbing to me all along.

However, before that happened I had the great privilege of playing in at least three Sunday matches down at The Vale. I know I definitely was not selected for one of them as I was asked to play for the opposition – always take your kit! I am not sure about the others but, anyway, the important thing was that I got to play. Realistically, the highest level I had hoped to achieve was to become a regular member of The Vale First XV; more enthusiastic than talented, I had started to play a little late for anything else. In terms of playing strength The Vale was a strong junior club at that time. Above them in the hierarchy were the senior clubs where standards went up a level and a step beyond that was the county side. In Lancashire, where county rugby was very important the players were mainly drawn from the leading senior clubs of Fylde, Waterloo, Preston Grasshoppers, Liverpool, Vale of Lune and later Orrell. It was from the top senior clubs across the country that the international players were drawn. Needless to say that this was another big step up. To us mere mortals this pool of players, especially the international players themselves, were the very gods of rugby. Yet they were human enough to come to The Vale to play us in Sunday matches and afterwards they even bought their own ale - mostly. Looking back it seems amazing that these guys were persuaded to turn up. (They didn't just play against The Vale but other junior and school sides as well throughout the season). On one occasion Mike Slemen of Liverpool and England turned up for a game which had been called off the previous evening due to the state of the pitch. No-one had been able to contact him. He was not in the least put out and adamantly refused to accept any expenses for his wasted journey.

For a number of years The Vale had regular fixtures against two such select teams each year: The Malcolm Phillips XV and The Shireburn Gentlemen. The participating players would have had a tough game on the Saturday and then on the Sunday would be on a hiding to nothing, knowing they would face fifteen players, albeit of lesser ability but hugely motivated. The difference in fitness levels then was not as great as it is today, since the advent of professionalism; I shudder to think of the consequences of going out on to the pitch in an equivalent fixture at the present time. I fear there would be mortalities among the mere mortals. However, we do not have to worry about that during this interlude.

The visiting Sunday teams followed the then prevailing Barbarian attitude towards penalty kicks at goal whilst The Vale tried to collect the points whenever we could; it was understood The Vale would do their utmost to win, and that they were not going to let us. Nevertheless, the games always seemed to follow a similar pattern. We would look pretty good during the first three quarters of the match. We would have some possession, do some attacking and get a few points on the board. At half time we would be thinking we were doing really well despite the fact we knew what was coming. If only we could keep going with a bit of luck we might just pull off an upset. The next twenty minutes would be tight with us straining every muscle and sinew and we would enter the last quarter down to a single score in the lead. The crowd would be getting excited as the clock ran down thinking we were in with a chance. Then suddenly the select side would turn it on with a slick piece of handling or some remarkable individual skill, score a couple of tries and with ten minutes to go it would be all over. Then they would show the crowd some exhibition rugby. Malcolm Phillips, of Fylde and England, once headed the ball out of his hands over an incoming tackler who was so astonished that he allowed him through to re-gather the ball and proceed to the try-line. Opinion on the touchline was divided as to whether it was a deliberate knock-on but in the opinion of the only person that mattered it was not; it was a Sunday match after all. Conversely, because it was Sunday some laws were more rigidly enforced. On one occasion, as he awarded a penalty where he had heard the offence take place, the referee announced,

"We'll have no bollocks on Sunday."

After the game The Ladies Committee served us with an excellent sit-down meal. We had a chance to get to know some of these giants of the game a little better and buy each other a pint or two. They had the good grace to seem like they enjoyed it almost as much as we did. Some insight what they may have been actually thinking may be had from the following words quoted from J.R.H. (Dick) Greenwood of Waterloo who, apart from being one of the leading lights of the Shireburn Gentlemen, also played for and captained England. In a club magazine he wrote :-

"The real pleasure, however, of accumulating fifteen masochistic eccentrics of tolerable quality for a bit of Sunday rugby has little to do with what goes on during the game but much to do with what goes on after ... To renew old friendships and seemingly just to pick up where last year's conversation left off, to play the game for real, but to keep it in proportion, and to sup ale in good company ..."

Those are sentiments which are impossible to fault. However, I believe there was more to it than that; more even than the legendary Vale hospitality. To all appearances at that time – appearances, that is, to us mere mortals as we had no real idea then what went on at Twickenham (or The Arms Park etc) – it was the top players who got the most out of rugby. Yet there was a strong ethic of the most fortunate giving something back to the sport. Those players who were coaxed, cajoled, bullied or blackmailed into giving up their Sunday afternoons might feel afterwards that, despite the extra bumps and bruises they would take to work the following day, they had enjoyed their little runabout. They would also be mindful of the pleasure they had given to the opposing players from the opportunity to pit themselves against their betters and they would be conscious of the entertainment they had provided for a reasonable crowd of spectators whose purchases at the bar boosted club funds. Last but not least, after the game at that bar they would be aware of having furthered the tradition of egalitarian fraternity within the sport whereby the lowliest practitioner had always been able to rub shoulders with the mightiest and even, if quick-witted enough when the chance came, to take the piss – in a respectful manner, of course.

134

Let's have a ride

"When I was a lad I was bicycle mad . . .
. . . I said, "My dear, if there's nobody near,
Let's have a ride on your bike."

When I joined the club The Vale players were, to a man, all good, honest, clean-living lads whose modest requirements for entertainment extended no further than a hard game of rugby and a couple of pints afterwards. (On special occasions it might have stretched to three). There may have been a time, years before, when The Vale might have called at a pub or two on their way back from matches and got up to some dubious antics but that was only a temporary deviation from the straight and narrow path set out by the founding fathers. That brief stray into the realm of unseemly adventures fuelled by an excess of beer had been corrected a generation ago by the strong leadership and personal example of a previous captain, (who might even have become a Methodist minister but for an unfortunate incident with the I.P.A. early on in his playing career). However, there were some Vale ancients who were aware that certain activities went on at other clubs, often after ridiculous amounts of ale had been consumed and when they heard I was undertaking a sociological study of amateur rugby union they insisted that I should include a chapter which covered these activities in order to give the reader the full, unretouched picture. They argued that the decorous situation at The Vale was exceptional and that I should not mislead the reader into thinking all rugby players were as clean-living as the lads from The Vale. This caused me a problem: for the simple reason that nothing ever went on at The Vale I had no personal experience of those things and my usual, reliable sources had no first-hand knowledge either. To gather the facts for the purposes of this study the net had to be cast further out; so far out, in fact, that it worried me that the shining light of truth, whose beacon has always guided my pen to the paper, might be dimmed by the murky waters I was obliged to trawl. Not to beat too much about the bush, I must warn you that I got all the stuff in the rest of this chapter from the lads at Colbourne. Even worse, I must make a further admission: to get it I had to ply them with ale. Consequently, I must alert the reader to the risk that in this chapter (and this chapter alone) I cannot vouch 100% for the truth; in fact, it could be as low as 95% in some parts. Sadly, there was no other way.

Before I approached the lads at Colbourne I had been worried that it might be tricky getting them to spill the beans. Nevertheless, being a firm believer that honesty is always the best policy, I was completely up front with them. I told them that the lads from The Vale had told me I needed to put in a chapter about the kind of thing that players from clubs like theirs got up to after the Vale lads had all gone home for the night. I anticipated some initial reticence as I had expected them to show some embarrassment even at Colbourne but it turned out that once sufficient lubrication had been administered they were openly prepared to brag about all kinds of things that would have made even Yul Brynner's[53] hair curl. In Colbourne phraseology the things they got up to were described as "atrocities" and it seems these atrocities were quite shamelessly committed on a regular basis. (I am really glad my playing days were spent at The Vale otherwise these Tales might have become just a succession of lurid accounts of post-closing time antics).

At this juncture I must give particular consideration to my younger reader who, I am hoping, may still be persevering. If so, he must be an inquisitive fellow, one who wants to acquaint himself with all aspects of the social history of our wonderful game and so he deserves additional consideration. He will be unable to understand the attitudes of that time without further guidance but the problem for me is to explain the chasm of difference which yawns like a black hole

---

[53] *Leading man of many American films, particularly "The King and I" (1956), as famous for his trademark completely shaven head as his performances.*

between then and now. A whole forest of footnotes would not suffice. The game of life has changed so completely that the young reader would be bewildered if he were to be transported back in time. He would scarcely be able to consider it credible that young men used to put themselves to such inconvenience and went to such expense in pursuit of what nowadays seems so readily available as long as you can be bothered. Faced with such a monumental turnaround I must embody the explanation in the main text.

First, the basic principles must be grasped: young men were expected to be rather keen on late night activities. That was considered both natural and manly. But young ladies were not expected to show any enthusiasm for them at all. That would have been considered unladylike. The intelligent young reader will immediately point out that there is an inherent contradiction here. Nevertheless, he must accept my assurance that not only was that the way it was but, as far as everyone at that time was aware, that was the way it had always been since Adam was a lad. Everybody was accustomed to it. They had grown up with it. They went along with it. They joined in the game and played the rules as they stood. (The fact that some not only failed to observe the rules but took delight in their own failure did not alter the fact that the rules, known collectively as "the done thing" existed). Over time, here and there, the odd adjustment to the rules would be made, one step at once, waiting for one change to be absorbed before making another (which is, in fact, what most people do unless, of course, they happen to sit on the Laws Study Group of the International Rugby Board). To give the younger reader a strong example of the done thing: if as a consequence of late night activities you fathered a child out of wedlock you were expected to contribute financially to its upbringing rather than let the State have the privilege. That was, of course, only if you were such a cad as to decline to pay the full price which was mutually understood to underwrite the transaction, namely, to enter into matrimony. (Obviously, none of the Vale lads was ever placed in the position of having to make that choice but I know, instinctively, they would have done the honourable thing).

In those days, practising safe sex meant trying your best not to get your girlfriend pregnant as often as she would let you; there was no such thing as casual sex; at the end of the day it was all deadly serious in its potential consequences.

Difficult though it may be the incredulous younger reader must grasp that essential principle as the key to understanding the cultural background to the double entendre, the innuendo and the smutty joke, all so popular at that time. However, I must admit that the times had begun a-changing even by the time my rugby playing days started. Life rumbles on more or less unchanged for donkey's years but such is the nature of our existence that its very foundations may be suddenly rocked by an earthquake and then, almost immediately, overwhelmed by a tsunami: no sooner had the Pill[54] become generally available than the Australian Dispensation Law was introduced[55]. The walls were not just rattled, the windows not just shaken; the glass was shattered and the walls tumbled. Things would never be what they used to be. The Pill brought the promise of freedom for girls in general and the change in the kicking law promised free-running rugby for the girls in the backs. Rugby Union became a more entertaining game for the layman to watch and people who had never played and hadn't a clue what was going on, started wasting space on the terraces at Twickenham. And women got cocky and started burning their bras.

---

[54] *Although in December 4, 1961, Enoch Powell, then Minister of Health, had announced that the oral contraceptive pill could be prescribed through the NHS at a subsidized price of 2s (10p) per month it took a while for the benefits to be felt at grass-roots level.*
[55] *This, initially experimental, change to the laws made in 1967 provided that if the ball was kicked directly (i.e. "on the full"), into touch in open play by a player standing outside his own 22 metre (then 25 yard) line the lineout was to be taken on a line from where the kick was made rather than from where it went into touch. It was made a permanent change after only one season.*

But I must get round to telling you about what happened when I met up with the "lads" from Colbourne. (Obviously, they were all knocking on a bit to be called lads but "old boys" has connotations which would not be appropriate and some slight poetic licence must be allowed even in a work of complete non-fiction such as this). I had arranged to meet them at a town centre pub. It had nothing to do with the fact that the beer was 50p a pint cheaper there: I thought it better we should have a neutral venue rather than one or other of the clubhouses and the beer's not so good at theirs anyway. They had arrived before me and I spotted them easily enough; they were all standing there with both hands in their pockets waiting for me to come and buy round. We started with the usual pleasantries: one of them jovially reminded me of the time I had dropped the ball when over their line. The others laughed politely for no more than five minutes. I didn't think it was just as funny as all that but I smiled benevolently; I was on a mission. I took it all in my stride. I let it pass. I could have mentioned the time when one of them could have been clean through but he fell for the yell of "inside" and donated a scoring pass to one of our lads. But I didn't; I remained above such pettiness.

They were a bit suspicious at first; my request seemed an unusual one from a former Vale player and they thought it might be a set up so that I could take the piss out of Colbourne in print. I had to assure them nothing was further from my thoughts and finally managed to persuade them, with the assistance of a pint or two, that my intentions were purely to record the importance of the mere mortal in the development of the game we all loved; inter-club rivalry wouldn't be allowed to interfere with that principle.

Having got over that hurdle, I explained that, although I was sure there was all sorts of useful material they could give me, I was particularly keen to learn what, in the context of après-match activities, was a "bicycle". This was because from snatches of conversation I had overheard in other clubhouses after away games I had come to understand that the word was not being used in its normal meaning. I realised there was something more to it than a pair of wheels and handlebars; for one thing mention of grips and saddlebags seemed to crop up more than I would have expected. Consequently, I had got an inkling that it might have something to do with those extra-post-match activities we eschewed at The Vale. My suspicions were confirmed when, on one occasion (also at an away match), I noticed that the popularity of one healthy-looking lass was increasing in inverse proportion to the time remaining to closing. When I heard her affectionately referred to as 'the eight-wheeler' I, quite naturally, enquired how she had come about this strange nickname. The answer was even stranger: I was told it was because she was several sizes too big to be a bicycle. I was completely puzzled and resolved to get to the bottom of it.

By way of response to my enquiry the Colbourne lads looked at me strangely and said why didn't I ask Matt Jinks who used to play at The Vale because he knew all there was to know about bicycles and plenty of other things besides. Obviously, they were trying to wind me up. I said the Matt Jinks era had been before my time but, anyway, he had moved away and nobody knew where he was. (I have a confession to make here as I actually know Matt Jinks better than I let on. A perfect gentleman. I can assure the reader that under no circumstances would he have become embroiled in anything untoward). However, it was important I didn't let them get to me because I had seen through the smokescreen - as the astute reader will already himself have seen: Colbourne were trying to dish the dirt so as to make The Vale appear on the same shady level as them. I'm afraid that this kind of finger-pointing hypocrisy was typical of the time.

One of them - I'll call him "John" for the sake of anonymity; he had been a scrum-half in his playing days, one of the chunky type with a low centre of gravity, which, I couldn't help but notice had got substantially lower with the passing years - continued,

"I didn't realise you were so much younger than you look. You must have known Pablo, though? I'm not saying he was a dirty bugger but he made Barnacle Bill[56] look like a gentleman."

"Well, once of a time," I retorted, "when he played for you lot he may have been but when he came to The Vale he was a reformed character." The shrewd reader will again be ahead of all this. Of course, Colbourne didn't like it when one of their players left to better himself at The Vale so blackening his name was just the kind of crude retaliation they would get up to. No foundation to it whatsoever.

"Reformed character!" John spluttered so much he must have wasted at least 30p worth of the beer I had just paid for. And they were all laughing again. Then it went quiet. I noticed they were all doing wrist exercises with their empty pint glasses so I got another round in. They were a subtle lot at Colbourne.

I remembered that when Pablo came to The Vale he had brought his nickname with him; I got the impression he didn't really like it but he would never let on how he had come by it. Foolishly, I let my longstanding curiosity get the better of me.

"How come he was called Pablo?" I asked.

Well, there was a smirk here and a knowing glance exchanged there. You don't have to be a highly trained bloodhound to know when someone's about to throw you an aniseed ball; I could see some variation of a latin lover gag coming a mile off just like my old mate, Mike, winding up to sell an outrageous dummy which, inevitably, always went back into stock. However, before John could reply, Bill, whom I remembered as a hard-tackling centre, especially after the ball had gone, butted in,

"As you will know Pablo was a teacher. In his younger days he had always fancied being an artist but his parents put the block on[57]. Anyway, one year the art teacher at his school was off sick, long-

---

[56] *The younger reader will find this mariner's romantic exploits described in detail in the mystery tale "Who's that Knocking at my Door" at page 46 of "Rugby Songs" published by Warner Books.*
[57] *In those days when parents had more influence over their children they tried to steer them into lines of study which might ultimately enable them to earn a living.*

term and Pablo jumped at the chance to step in to take the class. And that's how he got his name." He took a good gulp at his pint.

"How do you mean?" I asked, unable to see any obvious connection.

"If you'd let me finish. He used to like doing all that modern art stuff, extract paintings and such. He fancied he was good at it so when one day he overheard some of the kids referring to him as "Pablo" he took it as a big compliment. After Pablo Picasso, the famous Italian artist, you see. He really took it on, the whole thing. Grew a Zapata moustache and everything."

"A what moustache?" enquired Roger, another of the Colbourne lads. I won't say he was unintelligent even if he was a prop forward but one night, going home from Colbourne's clubhouse, he turned his back to the wind so he could light a fag and five minutes later he found himself back at the clubhouse again.

" A Zapata moustache. They named it after some guy who was a rebel in the Spanish Civil War."

It looked like Roger's cogs had been whirring but the mechanism had clearly failed to strike the bell.

"You know," Bill continued, seeing Roger was struggling, "like The Beatles. Nearly everybody had a do at it then. Flower power and all that. Anyway, he grew this droopy moustache and cultivated a sort of dago image. He looked a bit of a twit really because he had mousey-coloured hair and he was going a bit thin on top even then. It didn't suit him at all but then everybody took to calling him Pablo and he was really chuffed about it."

He paused, ostensibly to take a swig but I think, really, it was for dramatic effect.

"Then, one day, he found out the kids at his school had given him the name because he was a dead ringer for an ice cream chap who used to push a cart on the prom at Blackpool, 'Pablo's Perfect Ices' The tash came off straight away but the name still stuck."

He guffawed. I laughed politely. Obviously, they were making it all up. I don't suppose I'll ever find out the real reason how Pablo got his name. Worse, I felt I was getting nowhere despite a considerable outlay. So I pressed them again on the question of bicycles. There was a pause whilst yet more lubrication was administered.

"Well. How am I going to explain this?" said John, trying to look pensive. "You'll remember Ginny Wenkworth, won't you? Tall, blonde, absolute stunner," and he made an obscene gesture with his hands which I won't repeat here.

"What? At The Vale?" I replied. I had to be on the defensive here. I suspected they were up to their old finger-pointing tricks again; I knew there had never been any bicycles at The Vale. So I added:-

"No. I'm sure there was never anyone called Virginia at The Vale or, if there was, she couldn't have been there long."

"She wasn't called Virginia. They called her Ginny because if you asked her if she would like a drink she always had a large one and tonic with ice and lemon."

"Not your usual half of bitter or lager in a lady's glass then?"

"No. Not well trained at all. Very expensive. But nice work if you could get it."

"That was the problem," chimed in Bill. "You couldn't. She wasn't generally available for short term hire; she wanted to keep her mileage down whilst she was on the lookout for a permanent contract."

They were talking in riddles but at least there seemed to be a flow developing.

"You'd more chance with her friend. What was she called ...? Jane ...? Jane ...? Some unusual name, it was."

" Daugruffe."

" That was it. Jane Daugruffe. Those two always went round together, Wenkworth and Daugruffe."

"Jane was a lot more friendly."

"She had to be."

"You had a thing going there once didn't you, Roger?" Roger nodded, smiling nostalgically.

"Nay! Don't tell me his famous chat up line worked for once: 'what you having half of' ?" said John.

"Anything worked with her," added Bill

"Sod off!" said Roger. "She was all right was Jane ..."

This was it, I thought. The beer was working at long last. The conversation was livening up now. We could be getting down to the nitty gritty. But at the mention of Jane's name a strange, faraway look seemed to have come into Roger's eyes. Then I realised he was peering once more into his empty glass. I could scarcely believe it. I stumped up yet again.

"What really happened there, Roger?" asked John. "You spent so much time visiting The Vale we thought we were going to lose you to them at one stage."

"I got warned off in the end."

"How do you mean?"

"It was their skipper. Only looking after their fleet, I suppose. I had been overdoing it a bit. I think he thought I was going to take her out on long term hire."

"Bring her back to Colbourne, more like,"offered Bill. (They were always dreaming those lads at Colbourne).

"I was down at The Vale one evening, chatting her up in my own inimitable style ..."

"Nay! Not another half of bitter. More expense!"

"Will you sod off and stop interrupting! Anyway, he came over and said in his best, plummy accent, 'How nice to see you again, Roger. And how's the lovely wife? I trust she's recovering well after the twins. It was twins this time, wasn't it? Or was that last time? It's difficult to keep up with you.' The swine! Even Matt Jinks couldn't have talked her round after that."

"Matt Jinks!" John joined in. "Now there was a man who knew how to tell a girl what she wanted to hear. I was stood near to him once as he was chatting this bird up. He came out with this line. It made me cringe. I don't know how he kept his face straight. But that was it, I suppose, the mark of the master. Anyway she lapped it up. You could see her eyes going all gooey like a custard from Oddie's Bakery ... "

I had to butt in here. They were having another go at my old friend, Matt Jinks. I don't know what they had against him but it was, obviously, all nonsense and what was more they were straying off the subject yet again and funds were beginning to run low. I thought I would try a different approach.

"Does this bicycle business have anything to do with that old song?" I suggested.

They looked at me as blank as a Monday morning.

"What song?"

"You know," I said, *"Let's have a ride on your by – si – cal ... dar ... dar ... da dar da dee dar...Let's have a ride on your bike."*

I tried to extemporise with a few bars but their clocks told me it remained still way before 8.00am Monday morning as far as any celebral activity was concerned.

"You know," I encouraged, " it was a sort of folk song, I guess. It was about a young lad who pinched some woman's bike and she threatened to tell his father about it."

"No. No. You've got it all wrong there ; it sounds like a Max Miller[58] song to me – *dar dar dee dar dar dee dar dee dar* - but, hey! you know who that reminds me of?" Bill directed himself to the other two.

I also scanned the blank faces of the other two but they betrayed no sign of a synapse firing.

"You know . . . Mark Dickinson!" he persevered.

"Mark Dickinson ...?"

"Was he a big man for bicycles then?" I asked, trying to move things along.

"He certainly did have his moments," Bill replied. "I remember that time when we were up at ..."

"Mark Dickinson! Mark Dickinson! I remember him now," interrupted Roger. "Haven't seen him for years. Used to play full back. Star man. Didn't his brother play for us as well?"

---

[58]*Max Miller (1894 -1963), "the Cheeky Chappie", an old style music hall entertainer and comedian noted for his risqué humour and songs.*

"Only the once," said John, a grin starting to take control of his face.

"Bloody hell! That's right," said Bill, "I remember now . . ."

As he turned to confide further details in me I could see the big grin had infected him as well.

"Mark's brother was a soccer player but he came one week just before our game and he said Mark couldn't play for some reason; and as he'd no soccer game on that afternoon he'd come instead of Mark so we weren't short - which was good of him - and so we . . . we . . ." he tried to control himself but couldn't stop laughing. By now there was only me not wearing a big, silly grin and starting to shake.

" . . . we asked him where he wanted to play and he said he might as well play the same position as Mark, at full back because he'd watched him once. And he did all right to start with. But then they punt a high ball. He gets underneath it all right ... " - by now we were being treated to a visual re-enactment – "eyes on the ball, hands and arms ready, cradled to catch it ... catches it, makes a mark and then ..." John's voice was now rising to a squeaky crescendo, "... and then he yells "Andrew!" at the top of his voice and stood his ground ... but ... but ... but their pack just trampled over him ... and ... and ..."

He had to put his pint down at this stage as he was in danger of spilling the bit that was left he was shaking so much with laughter.

"... all our lot collapsed laughing and they scored under the posts."

By now tears of remembrance were running down all their faces.

"But he was really annoyed about it. We asked him afterwards what he had done that for. It turned out it was something to do with the rules in soccer. You can't just call for the ball you have to give a name. When watched his brother play rugby once he'd called for a mark and he thought he was calling his own name out. So, fair play when he caught the ball he called "Andrew!" and got flattened for his trouble. He was not impressed. It took a long time and a lot of beer after the game before he even started to see the funny side of it but he

146

still said he had always thought rugby was a barmy game and he should have known better than get involved. He never came to play again."

I must admit I thought it was a good story and remembering it really seemed to put the Colbourne lads into a good humour. It must have done because they started to get rounds in. Then, at last, they started telling me all about bicycles and atrocities and all kinds of things some of which might even have shocked the younger reader. But I got writer's cramp and couldn't take any more notes. I wasn't too bothered at the time because I was sure I would remember everything but then when I came to start writing it down the following day I found I couldn't remember just exactly what was said and who said what. As there is no way I would want to put anything into print about such a good set of lads that I wasn't absolutely sure about one hundred per cent I have decided the best thing to do would be to arrange another meeting. In the meantime, if there is any reader who knows anybody who knows something about bicycles please get him to send me some details.

Team Spirit

There was a young man named Paul
Who had a hexahedronal ball
And the square of its weight
Times his pecker plus eight
Was the height he could piss up a wall.

"Some car you've got there, Johnny!" exclaimed Kevin, examining the coachwork of the big, gleaming black Daimler.

"I bet it uses some petrol," said Keith.

"Shut up," stage-whispered Paul. "We'll be having to contribute next."

"Don't worry," said Johnny. "I fill her up on the firm."

"That's a relief," said Kevin who was an apprentice and found that Saturdays in the rugby season made serious inroads into his budget. They were waiting for Frank and Harry who both worked Saturday mornings and always struggled to get there in time for the scheduled departure for away matches. The big Daimler would be the last to set off but, with all those horses under the bonnet, they soon expected to catch up.

The Vale's fortunes had begun to rise slowly since the end of the war but even as the end of the fifties approached the selection committee still needed to ensure that enough car owners were picked to provide the transport to away games. Some asked to be reimbursed for petrol expenses; others did not bother. The club had found it difficult to get going again after the war: some of the older players had not resumed and fewer younger ones had come through. Shirts were found to be moth-eaten and the stitching on the balls had gone rotten during the long lay-off. Money for the necessary replacements had been in short supply especially as funds had also been needed to bring the pitch and changing facilities back into use. Furthermore, King Cotton's faltering reign, briefly reprieved by the war, was quickly drawing to a close and the area was finding it hard to diversify into other industry. They were difficult times and The Vale's struggles mirrored those of the area it belonged to.

After one particularly disastrous playing season due to a shortage of players the unthinkable had not only been thought but voiced and a merger with local rivals, Colbourne, had been proposed at a specially called crisis meeting. Peering over the abyss had stiffened resolve and the members had been galvanised to redouble their efforts to recruit new playing members. The greater part of those efforts had necessarily to be directed towards the conversion of soccer players of whom there were literally thousands in the area; they had the advantage of already owning a pair of boots. But anyone appearing to possess the attributes, more normally associated with those east of the border, of being "strong i't'back and weak i'th'ead" was also considered likely material. The standard approach was:-

"I can't believe a big, strong lad like you isn't already playing rugby!"

These were times, of course, when the idea of using child psychology as a persuasive tool was in its infancy. Nevertheless, it rarely worked; even inarticulate Jehovah's Witnesses have had better success rates. But to every rule there are exceptions and the passengers of the Daimler, when everybody arrived, would consist of two big, useful lads who had not played until their adult lives.

Harry was last to arrive and was greeted warmly by Paul:-

"Bloody hell: they haven't picked you again, have they?"

"Never mind me. You just concentrate on playing better than you did last week. It shouldn't be difficult"

"Just tell me you haven't forgotten your wallet again this week. I'm sick of having to buy you beer."

"That'll be the day. I wouldn't know whether to sup it or frame it if I ever got a pint off you. A duck's arse doesn't come near it."

The conventional pleasantries concluded, the passengers embarked and the car set off towards the big city where, at one of the many clubs on its outskirts the day's game was to be played.

"Leather seats as well! I could get used to travelling in this kind of style. Where did you get it Johnny?"

"We bought it from Thorneyholmes, the old weaving company. They've gone into liquidation. It was their M.D's car."

"Plenty of that happening. Still it's an ill wind. I must say it's very comfortable. Lots of room even with these two gorillas in the back. Seems to have been well looked after."

As they passed through town Paul practised his regal wave on the Saturday afternoon shoppers. One elderly lady turned to stare, wondering who could possibly be waving at her from such a fancy motor. Instinctively, she began to raise a hand, half-minded to wave back which was much to the amusement of the other passengers who then waved like idiots at her through the back window. Having passed through the town, the car started to climb one of the hills surrounding the valley. It was a long steep drag which the big car tackled effortlessly until the summit was almost reached but then the engine started to miss.

"I thought somebody said this car was well maintained."

"That's strange..." said Johnny. "Oh hell! I know what it is: we're running out of petrol."

"I thought you said you filled her up on the firm?"

"I do. That is I was going to fill her up this morning but then something happened and I forgot."

"You dozy bugger."

"Big flash car and no juice. All fur coat and no knickers!"

"Come on, old girl ... If we can just get to the top..."

Tantalisingly short of the summit the engine cut out completely and the car quickly ground to a halt. Johnny applied the handbrake.

"What are we going to do now?"

"Well, we can't go back down anyway," said Johnny. "The brakes work off a servo. If the engine's not running we could end up in Anderton's shop window at the bottom, like that wagon did last year."

"That's great! We're the last. There's nobody else going to be coming past."

"There's five of us," said one of the big lads. "If we can just push her to the top we should be able to free-wheel down the other side. There's a petrol station just down the hill."

"You're joking! The weight of this thing! No chance."

But the other big lad and the others were already out of the car.

"Come on!" they shouted. "We can do it!"

So two big strong men and three others lined up behind the heavy car on a steep hill as Johnny gingerly released the handbrake. Gradually, it began to move forward but it was hard work and slow progress. They kept going as long as they could. They did not want to stop as they knew it would be even harder to get going again but, eventually, there were more grunts per inch than in a piggery at feeding time and Johnny yanked the handbrake on again as they came to a dead stop. There was still some way to go. After a rest they had another go which did not get them as far as the first shove had done. Then another. They were spurred on by shouts of mock encouragement and toots of derision from the horns of cars full of football supporters passing the other way to watch the First Division soccer match in town. Seeing the blazer-wearing occupants of a big, fancy car having to push was an entertainment in itself and it was free. They would still be chuckling when they got into the many pubs near the ground for a pre-match pint or two, "You should have seen those posh buggers ..."

In the end they made it although there was no wind left for anything but the feeblest cheer as they reached the summit and then gravity began to take over.

Your memory always tells you that, once you get over the brow of the hill, it is downhill all the way to the petrol station. In reality this is never the case. The road starts off going down, sure enough, but round the bend and before the petrol station, which is, in any case, always further away than you thought, it goes up again before it continues to descend. Without the servo Johnny dare not let the Daimler free-wheel entirely and despite the voluble encouragement of the passengers, whose lungs were recovering, it glided to a halt once more on the next incline amongst a welter of expletives. The five were obliged to get out and push again.

It was not as steep this time so they were able to manage to get to the next downhill bit in one go but they were all panting like polar bears in a heat wave by the time they got into the car again.

"I don't know how the hell we're going to be able to play rugby after this," said Frank. "I hope there aren't any more flipping hills."

"It won't make any difference to you anyway - unless you've miraculously improved since last week."

152

"Sod off!"

No matter what the circumstances The Vale lads were always guaranteed to come up with a quick-witted riposte even in those days.

Fortunately, there were no more hills and the petrol station at last came in view. Thankfully, it was open and, by chance, there was a pub next door. Undeterred by the unpromising exterior, whilst Johnny was filling her up, two of the company went straight in; they had been in less salubrious establishments before. They were soon followed by the others.

"We shouldn't be doing this, you know," said one. "Drinking before the game's been outlawed since Henshaw was captain."

"This is an emergency," declared Paul. "Not only am I as dry as a witch's tit I am completely knackered. I need a couple of pints and a rest."

"We don't want to get back to the old days when they used to go on the piss before the game. They lost nearly every match then," cautioned Harry.

"That was different. They had to do it then."

"How do you mean?"

"They were that short of players that if they hadn't kept the boozers happy they wouldn't have been able to put a team out. The club would have folded and you would have had nowhere to play. And don't say you would have gone to Colbourne."

"Anyway there's vitamins and carbohydrates in beer."

"Carbo – whats?"

"Carbohydrates. Like sugar. Give you energy."

"You could certainly do with some of that, judging by last week's performance. I've seen more movement in a frozen scarecrow on a still day."

"Piss off!"

Out of the smoke at the other end of the bar came a voice:-

"You lads play rugby?"

"Some of us do. Some just come for the day out."

"Rough game that," said the voice. "I'd have liked to have played myself but I was too small."

"Size doesn't matter ..."

The Vale player was about to justify his assertion when the man, considering that he had successfully introduced himself into the conversation, sidled over and The Vale player paused: he had been mistaken in thinking the man had been sitting down. He had brought with him his empty glass and, realising he was on the cadge, Johnny fell soft and bought him a half. It didn't earn them a complete reprieve from the life story - it was no surprise to hear that at one time he had been a jockey - but, having got his half, the man soon went back to his paper to continue studying form. There were several others quietly doing the same and when the lads looked round they noticed nicotine stained items of racing memorabilia hanging on the walls: jockeys' caps, silks, whips and photographs of racehorses. Then somebody pointed out the time and consciences were pricked: kick-off time was approaching and they were still a good way from the ground. As they drained their glasses they heard the man's voice again:-

"I've got a good one for you here: Team Spirit. It's in the 3.30 at Haydock. I know the trainer. He's bringing it up all the way from down South. He's not doing that for nothing. It's the only horse he's got running at Haydock today. That's where my money's going this afternoon. I'd get some money on yourselves if I were you."

"Team Spirit, eh ?" said Johnny. "That sounds just like The Vale. What do you reckon? Why don't we all put half a dollar on?"[59]

"*How* much?" said Kevin.

"What? Each? That's nearly two pints," Frank spluttered.

"Tell you what," said Johnny. "We put two shillings each in apart from the apprentice. He's in but he doesn't have to pay. That gives us a kitty of ten shillings. Five bob each way. Team Spirit! It's bound to win."

After some further muttering the kitty was collected.

"Where's the nearest bookie's?" they asked the tipster.

"You don't need bother with the bookie's," said the man. "You can put it on here. The landlord rings the bets through and he'll give you a slip."[60]

---

[59] *Half a dollar was half a crown: two shillings and sixpence pre-decimalisation or 12p in today's money.*

It seemed dubious but they were already late so Johnny asked:-

"All right but where do we collect our winnings?"

"You can collect them here. The landlord has an arrangement with the bookie; he's a relation of his. It's like a service for the regulars."

Despite a hard stare from Frank, Paul handed over the ten shillings. They left and settled back into the limousine.

"That was some dive."

"Tell me I imagined it," Frank said. "We didn't really just hand over ten bob, did we?"

"It'll be right. The landlord's obviously on a rake-off from the bookie plus it keeps them in there drinking. He's not going to do anything to spoil that. He's on a winner both ways," said Paul.

"Which will be more than can be said for us," said Frank.

"Hey! Did you see that woman?" Keith asked.

"That dress were a bit low cut for a Saturday dinner!"

"A bit? You could see nearly all she'd got."

"Especially when she lent over."

"Dirty bugger! Shouldn't have been looking."

"When it's all in the shop window it would be rude not to."

"Do you reckon she was on the game?"

"She was definitely eyeing Rockefeller here up. Thought he'd be good for a quid or two."

"I couldn't tell who she was eyeing up; one eye was on main beam and the other on dipped."

"She did sken a bit."

"A bit? Even you'd struggle to look her in the eye and tell her you loved her."

"Sod off!"

---

[60] *It was illegal to place bets other than at a bookmaker's premises.*

By the time the six were changed and on the field The Vale, who, after delaying the start as long as the ref would allow, had had to kick off with only nine men, were down a good few points and they were unable to recover the deficit despite their best efforts. It did not go down well with the captain and he approached the six after the game with the intention of administering a good bollocking. However, he could not say too much after he had been told about the running out of petrol, especially as Johnny had paid for it anyway and he knew he never asked for any money back. Of course, they had conveniently forgotten to tell him about the subsequent need for refreshments. Nevertheless, although the description of the heroic effort of pushing the big car uphill was drawn out like a fisherman's tale the captain suspected that there was more to it than he was being told especially as two of the latecomers had been smelling ferociously of mint when they had scrummed down.

The air of lingering suspicion, which seemed to be shared by the other eight Vale players, contributed to the lack of the usual after match conviviality and the six decided they would make early tracks.

As they passed through the centre of the suburb nearest to the ground, Kevin spotted a street news vendor and shouted,

"Stop. Let's get a pink."[61]

"What for? The football results?"

"No. I want to see how Team Spirit has gone on."

The car drew up at the kerb and coppers were exchanged through the window for a copy of the newspaper.

"It's won! Fuck me!"

"No, thanks. Not whilst there's dogs on the street in Colbourne."

"What odds?"

"Twelve to bloody one!"

"You're joking. How much have we won?"

---

[61] *Before everyone had a television the Saturday's sports results would be printed in a special evening edition often on pink or green paper. It would be on the streets within an hour of matches finishing, the local vendors shouting "Pink!" It was handy for checking your pools and the racing results in the pub Saturday evening.*

"We should get about four quid back, I reckon."

"If we get it," said Frank.

Earlier, when the bet had been placed they had done it more as a reaffirmation of their belief in The Vale than in serious expectation of a win so the irregularity of the arrangement they had entered into had not caused them a great deal of worry. After all, it was only two shillings each. But now four pounds hung in the balance it suddenly seemed appropriate to be concerned about the security of their investment. The chauffeur was requested to make all haste back to The Nags Head.

The landlord did not seem as pleased to see them as he had earlier and their fears were confirmed when they produced the betting slip he had given them. He looked apprehensively at the two big, useful lads,

"Sorry lads. Just about everybody in the pub backed that one. I'm out of cash for now ... No ... wait a minute. Don't worry: you'll get your money. As soon as I've got some takings I'll pay you out. It's early yet and there's no money in the till but if you can just wait a bit..."

"That's a poor do," said Paul. "When will they start coming in?"

"Any time now. I tell you what: I'll start a slate for you if you like. Then you can have a drink whilst you're waiting."

They had heard worse ideas and they might as well get something out of it so it was soon agreed. The landlord looked at the slip.

"Five bob each way at twelve to one plus your stake back that's four pound five shillings you've got to come."

"You know," said Johnny. "It's amazing how they work these things out. I knew a lad at school who would take thirty seconds to come up with the answer to two times two and say five. Within a month of leaving school and taking an apprenticeship, he could tell you what you would get for a sixpenny bet on a reverse yankee doubled with an each way forecast, to the penny, within the blink of an eye."

"It's right, though," said Frank who had worked it out on the back of a beermat. "Four pounds five shillings. We're in for a good night."

The quality of the ale was in inverse proportion to the surroundings and it soon started to go down very well but they had forgotten that the big Daimler was parked conspicuously outside. They had intended only to collect their winnings and have a swift one – it would have been bad manners not to. The car was spotted by some more of the Vale contingent as they passed. Naturally, they wanted to know what the others were doing in that dive, The Nag's Head. The six already ensconced tried to bluff that they had heard about the ale being so good but when one of the new arrivals noticed that they were not actually paying for their beer the story eventually came out. The newcomers all demanded pints off the slate as the price of silence.

The existence of the slate had not gone unnoticed, either, by the lady in the low-cut dress who had returned for the evening session, looking even more glamorous than she had done earlier. She found no difficulty in joining the company and being included within the largesse of the high rollers. Some of the more enterprising Vale lads hit upon a solution to the roving eye problem by focussing instead on her ample cleavage and they continued to buy her drinks long after the slate had been wiped clean. Despite, no doubt, being aware that she was growing more attractive by the pint, she had realised the improbability of concluding any business that evening but she was clever enough to have a weighed up that the two big lads were suckers for child psychology. Exactly how she came round to the theme I can't imagine – perhaps the lateness of the hour minimised the need for subtlety or delicacy - but when it came to it her gambit, in its simplicity, was:-

"I bet you two quid you can't piss higher than me."

The lads rolled about, thinking it was a huge joke.

"You're not shy, are you?"

The lads stopped laughing when they realised she was serious. Even setting aside questions of masculine honour, they were confident of extending their winning streak – how could they lose - and the bet was taken on, the lads to win if either of them made the highest mark. The lady insisted the same rules had to apply to both sides to which The Vale lads readily agreed.

A piece of chalk was borrowed off the dart board and the contestants, followed by the spectators, went out into the dimly lit yard at the back of the pub where the gents' urinals were situated. A line was chalked on the flags a couple of feet from the red brick wall of the toilets.

Naturally, the order was ladies first. She turned her back to the wall, lined the backs of her heels up with the chalk line and bent over. Then, having taken the opportunity to remove her knickers earlier, lifted her skirt over her back and urinated against the wall. The adjudicator quickly stepped up to mark the level of highest point on the wall with the chalk. It was not impressive; perhaps a little more than three feet. Grinning broadly at having nothing to beat and in the anticipation of the second lot of winnings for the day, The Vale's heroes stepped up to the line and prepared to register their marks.

"Just a moment!" said the lady as they prepared to take aim. "We agreed the same rules for both sides. No hands!"

The Ram's Head

Sausages and sauce are the words which spring to mind these days when Cumberland is mentioned. For centuries a proud county in its own right, Cumberland morphed into Cumbria in 1974 when it was amalgamated with Westmorland and also with the Furness peninsula which had previously been part of Lancashire. There must be many other things apart from gastronomic items to which Cumberland has given its name but we are concerned here with only one: the Cumberland Foot-rush. This tactic, which may have had its origins in mediaeval football, had more or less died out in most parts of the country – possibly due to the vagaries of the bounce of the modern rugby ball, but in the era when the events to be related took place the foot-rush was still used with enthusiasm and vigour in Cumberland and the neighbouring county of Westmorland. A phalanx of forwards would form up behind the ball and dribble it on between them. The movement would start slowly and gather controlled momentum. Fly-hacking had to be avoided as it was vital that the ball did not get kicked too far ahead of the chasing pack. Given that conditions were usually wet and the ball as slippery as a double glazing salesman it was often more effective than a handling movement.

You might think that the foot-rush would provide an excuse to kick the shit out of anyone who got in the way, especially if the referee was positioned behind the pursuing phalanx but, of course, that kind of thing never happened in the good old days. Well, not deliberately. However, as you might expect the majority of rugby players in Cumberland and Westmorland used to be farmers; in fact, in the team The Vale was on its way to play on the day when the incidents of which I am about to tell took place, just about every one of them was a farmer, apart, of course, from the usual disproportionate number solicitors. Now farmers, unlike townsfolk, are used to the wide open spaces; they can park their tractors where they please and as they always wear wellies they don't have to worry too much where they put their feet. Consequently, they can get a bit careless about the exact placement of their plates. I've no doubt that on a Saturday afternoon they did their best to be more careful but accidents will happen. Before every match The Vale played in the region the skipper of the day would always advise that if the opposition should start a foot-rush the best way to minimise the risk of an accident was to drop on the ball immediately and nip the movement in the bud because if the farmers got into their stride they found it even more difficult than usual to control the swinging boot.

There was no fuss made as The Vale's coach rattled over the border into Westmorland; it was not like crossing into Yorkshire. Besides, everyone's mood was lightened by the sparkling day: shafts of sunlight beamed through the coach windows and caught the rising dust particles in lazy swirls. It was a bit of a rickety old coach that week and not the usual driver. In the interests of economy, which was always a major concern, the committee had decided to try a different company. But nobody on the coach was bothered. How could they be on such a day? The tiniest wisp of white cloud only served to emphasise the azure of the sky. The countryside was beginning to cast off winter's drab, beige overcoat to show the just-minted softness of spring's early green, so refreshing and cool on the eye. There was a promise in the air which told that the year had turned. The Vale lads would have heard the joy in the birdsong had the coach's engine not been making such a racket but, nevertheless, they could see the birds through the window as they followed the age-old rituals of spring, carrying a twig here and a feather there. In short, it was such a wonderful and stirring spring day that a full-blooded young man's thoughts could not help but turn to the forthcoming tour at Easter, now only a couple of weeks away.

But the tour was not the only topic of conversation that day; a sore point in the Vale psyche had been prodded again by shocking revelations from the previous weekend. The long-standing grievance concerned a rather unusual and attractive item, considered an heirloom, which had adorned a place of honour on the wall in Vale's clubhouse for many a long year. Although it was difficult to tell the materials it was made out of and what the original colours had been due to the layers of nicotine with which it had been coated over the years its intrinsic charm was unmistakeable: it exhibited two players standing beneath a splendidly straight set of posts, each with one arm round the other whilst one cradled a rugby ball in his free arm and the other raised a pint with his free hand. If one picture is worth a thousand words this icon, being in 3-D must have been worth quite a few noughts more on the end. To the Vale lads, as a handsomely crafted epitome of the game they loved, it was priceless. The details of how and when it had first come to be displayed at the clubhouse had passed beyond living memory; it had been there so long that its provenance no longer mattered even though anyone who cared to make a close inspection might have noted inscribed on it in small letters "Presented to Harlequins R.F.C by W.W. Ellis".

No, the only problem with the trophy as far as The Vale was concerned was that it had gone; it wasn't there any more. What was worse was that it transpired that nobody had a clue who had taken it or when. The sad loss had been discovered three years ago; a member happened to look up from his pint at the nicotine-free silhouette which had been screaming "Theft!" for weeks and casually enquired of his companion why the trophy was not in its usual place. The other speculated that the steward had probably taken it down for the cleaning it so badly needed but when the steward was asked he was sure that someone from the committee had taken it down for that very same purpose. However, no one from the committee knew anything about it. Incredulity added to the sense of loss; it was like someone had stolen the Town Hall clock. How could they not have noticed? After the initial shock many an evening was spent round the bar in enquiry and speculation. Lists of the usual suspects were drawn up – only Colbourne could be left out: The Vale always watched them like hawks when they visited and, besides, if they had got it, it was unthinkable that none of them would have crowed about it. In the end they just had to accept that they had no idea who had done it: it could have been more or less anyone which prompted an older member to grumble about the sorry state things had come to. "No one can be trusted to keep their hands off anything these days; nothing is sacred," he said. "It's disgraceful."

For weeks if not months every player had gone round with his eyes peeled and his ears cocked. Surely, some vital snippet of information would come their way; somebody would be heard boasting or the trophy would be spotted at another clubhouse. But no clues did come and after a while the matter had slipped from the forefront of people's minds. That was until the previous week when one of the Vale lads had been visiting his in-laws up in Cumberland over the weekend. Not wishing to exhaust the delights of his hosts' company all in one go he had managed to get a game with the local club. It was a club which neighboured Chapelton Lunesdale, the club The Vale were going to play that day and those two clubs enjoyed a similar rivalry to that between The Vale and Colbourne. After the match the Vale lad had heard suspicions voiced by his teammates of the day that players from Lunesdale had removed a trophy from their club in a sneaky manner. It was something which in the natural order of things caused no wheels to spin within the brain of the visitor but they certainly crashed into gear when they went on to say that Lunesdale were in the habit of taking the trophy down from display in their clubhouse and hiding it whenever they had a fixture against its rightful owners. The extent of this deviousness shook the Vale player to the core – as it did all those listening to his story on the coach as it rattled along that day. Such behaviour was definitely not within the spirit of whatever governed that kind of thing.

Amongst those listening intently to this story of infamy was Wilf, (not his real name, of course), a man of many talents when it came to post-match entertainment and a past master not just at concocting hare-brained schemes but at persuading others to carry them out so that when the crunch came he was well out of range of the fallout from the rotating blades. As he listened he convinced himself that Lunesdale, who had not figured on any of the short lists of suspects which had been drawn up, were not only responsible for The Vale's missing trophy but also that, despite the fact that relations between the two clubs had always been most cordial, they were capable of stooping so low as to hide the trophy away, thus denying

The Vale the sporting chance of recovering it by any legitimate means. A plot began to incubate in his fertile brain.

By the time the coach ground its way into the car park at the opposition clubhouse – it was the very same place where some years before a young and green Sicky Binns had failed ignominiously in his attempt to retain the four pints of Youngers I.P.A. he had been encouraged by those he thought his elders and betters to consume between entering the bath and leaving it – Wilf had the firm outline of a plausible plan as well as the identities of his supporting cast in mind. They would be Badger, second row and The Vale's senior line-out jumper, Ben, the scrum-half with his reliable, quick pass and Jimmy who partnered him at stand-off. Jimmy had a good, safe pair of hands even if he could be a bit unpredictable once he had got the ball in them. Wilf would have to make sure Jimmy knew exactly what he had to do but he couldn't see a problem there; the plan was simple enough. All Wilf needed to do then was to reassure himself that he remembered correctly the layout of the clubhouse: that part was crucial to his plan.

Having deposited the Vale teams, the driver coaxed his vehicle, which, by the sound it was making, was never going to complete the return journey without some immediate attention, off the car park again, expressing a confident hope that the necessary repairs could be carried out in the nearby town.

As the teams passed through to the changing rooms Wilf, looking for all the world like an Indian scout in civvies, discreetly made his reconnoitre of the clubhouse. As he had expected there was no sign of the Vale trophy. Neither was there any tell-tale space or nicotine shadow to indicate where it might have recently resided but he didn't allow that minor detail to trouble him; he felt an unstoppable momentum akin to that of the foot-rush building up. Secondly, he confirmed that, as he had thought, the clubhouse was divided into two rooms by double doors and, finally, he noted with satisfaction that the ram's head with its splendid horns was still hanging above those doors. His plan was coming together; he just needed a quiet moment to think it through.

It is necessary for me here to interrupt the narrative to describe the ram's head and to explain its significance. It was a magnificent specimen. It had been donated years ago by one of the club's stalwarts who had been the ram's owner. He had taken a vicarious pride in the fact that in its long and happy professional career the ram had sired in excess of twenty thousand, three hundred and eighty two lamb chops – a record number which seemed to grow exponentially each time the story was told. Despite the fact that this had nothing to do with rugby whatsoever, over the years the ram had come to be regarded as a kind of testament to the virility of the club members and after it had departed to the happy tupping grounds its owner had spared no expense in having its head mounted on a carved plaque of the finest oak which he had presented to the club. It had been installed with great ceremony in a prominent position above the double doors; everything had been done to ensure that in death it was as it had been in life: extremely well hung.

The quiet moment Wilf needed came sooner than he had expected. Despite the skipper's warning a foot-rush was allowed to develop early on in the game and the Vale full back was confronted by the not-pretty sight – at any stage of the game – of several hefty north country farmers in full cry, hotly pursuing the ball. He dived bravely to collect the ball but at the same time collected a boot to the head. The injury was beyond the capacity of the magic sponge and its assistant to repair and the unfortunate player had to be temporarily removed from the field of play whilst one of the home supporters ran him down to the local vet's to be stitched. Whilst play was stopped – and I will mention here for the benefit of any reader who has never played rugby (just in case there is one for I am, by nature, an optimist) that an injured player was always clapped off the field by all the players and spectators and clapped back on again if he was able to return. I always thought this was a nice touch with its echoes of ancient chivalry and I particularly appreciated it when I was playing on the wing as it gave me a chance to get my hands warm on a cold day without drawing attention to myself. (Similarly, anyone who returned to consciousness after an application of the magic sponge also received a round of applause in respect of the entertainment provided. But I digress).

Whilst play was stopped Wilf was putting the final touches to his plan. There was no doubt in his mind now that it was going to be both effected and effective. He was satisfied the plan was good, one of his best, in fact, and any qualms about the justification – not that he ever suffered greatly from these – had been washed away by the blood which had flowed from his team-mate's head. He knew it had been an accident, of course, but even accidents require compensation and the ram's head would do nicely.

The game resumed and you would have thought that all the players, having witnessed the result of one piece of carelessness, would have been encouraged to be more careful but, perversely, the result was the opposite. First The Vale's players lapsed into a bout of carelessness and then the opposition, no doubt thinking, "if you're not going to be more careful then we jolly well won't be either," followed suit and one of the more robust encounters between the two sides resulted.

All this worked to Wilf's advantage: when he explained his plan to his key personnel, the line-out jumper, the scrum-half and the fly-half, after the game he found it easy to overcome any reservations they would normally have had - they had been involved in Wilf's schemes before. However, not only were they animated by what had gone on in the match but they could see a larger degree of simplicity and, therefore, a greater chance of success in the plan than was usually present in Wilf's machinations. The gist was this: whilst Wilf created a distraction in the room furthest from the entrance to the clubhouse one of the dividing double doors would be surreptitiously closed – closing both might have aroused suspicion – the closed door would shield Badger, the jumper, from view. Then he would leap and, using both hands, dislodge the ram's head and in the same silky movement throw it down to the waiting scrum-half, Ben, who would whip out a long pass to Jimmy, the fly-half, who would be standing at the entrance to the clubhouse. The latter would then dash outside and hide it in a place from which it could be recovered later. This would all happen so quickly that no one would notice. Wilf's role, as he pointed out, was pivotal even though he would not actually be in the thick of the action himself. He said it was essential that all eyes should be on him at the crucial moment. He had no doubts about his own ability to pull off this aspect of the scheme for he had acquired a widespread reputation as the instigator of post-match antics which ensured a welcome wherever he played. He also had a good memory for faces and was confident that there was no-one amongst the opposition who had ever seen the three-man-lift. The three-man-lift was the pièce de résistance of the Vale repertoire and as such was only performed occasionally in order to preserve its mystique. Today would be just the day for it. It was certain to draw them all in and, even better, it only required a couple of trusted helpers. Like many a military strategist before him Wilf had decided that the fewer he let into the plot the better. He was happy; all that mattered now was to get the timing right.

Any disagreements from on the field were soon dissolved in the traditional manner off it but Wilf and his co-conspirators took care not to be seduced by the charms of the Youngers I.P.A.

Meanwhile, although it had been noticed that the coach had not yet returned, for the moment its absence caused no concern; it was, obviously, still being repaired in the village.

As soon as Wilf was satisfied that the mood was right he appointed himself master of ceremonies in the far room where he immediately established a following. With a mixture of banter, challenges and calculated insults to the opposition and the introduction of new games he succeeded in making himself the centre of attention. In a short time he had gathered everyone into the room and was in complete control of the situation. Then encouraging nods from the scrum-half told him that his co-conspirators were taking up their positions. It was time for Wilf to play his ace. "Who," he asked the opposition, "is man enough to attempt the three-man-lift? There is only one person outside The Vale who has ever been able to do it but there look to be some good strong lads here today and with the help of my two experienced assistants here they might have half a chance. Who is going to give it a go?"

Now the thing about the three-man-lift, for anyone who doesn't already know, is that in order to achieve a satisfactory result not only must the preparation be careful but it must be drawn out for as long as possible to heighten the drama but without, of course, risking losing the audience's attention. In this case it was vital that no one should leave the room. It was a fine line but Wilf was equal to the task; in fact, he was in his element.

Soon he noted that one of the doors had been quietly closed and when he saw Badger's raised thumb appear around the side of the door as arranged, he knew it was time for the final part of the plot to be enacted. It was his cue to start the three-man-lift. Meanwhile, in the other room, with a mighty spring the jumper became airborne. He seemed to hover gracefully in the air as both hands grasped the trophy. In fact, he did hover in the air for, as previously mentioned, the ram's head was extremely well hung. But when an irresistible force meets an immoveable object something has to give and a couple of good strong screws had to give best to the sixteen stone forward. Unfortunately, with exquisite timing, Lunesdale's President, who for the last few minutes had been pitting his desire to see the denouement of the three-man-lift against the urgings of his bladder, decided he could wait no longer. As he hurried through the open half of the doorway on his way to the toilet he was comprehensively beaned by the ram's head as it descended. Commendably, the scrum-half did not allow himself to be distracted by this attempted interception but calmly gathered the rebound and whipped out as good a pass to the fly-half as he had made all season.

Naturally, both the second row and the scrum-half immediately went to the aid of the stricken President but the commotion had been such that not even Wilf and the three-man-lift could prevent an exodus from the other room to see what had happened. It seemed that many of the home members were desirous of an explanation as to why their President came to be lying on the floor semi-conscious and bleeding from a head wound. Foul play was not, of course, suspected and no doubt the President would have explained it was all an accident but when he came round all he could remember was that he was desperate for a piss and, having attended to that need, he was immediately whisked off to the vet's for repairs.

Badger maintained The Vale's reputation for honesty and never telling a lie; he said he had not seen *exactly* what had happened. The scrum-half took advantage of his slight stature to merge into the background and say nothing. When the fly-half reappeared after depositing the trophy in a safe place of concealment he made it look like he had just been to the toilet. Wilf pointed to the floor and suggested, "Perhaps he could have slipped on this spilt beer." And, indeed, it was noticed that there was a spillage. (It might have been more convincing had it been a larger spillage but Wilf always was a man of frugal habits). However, that explanation was not sufficient to prevent the men from Westmorland from casting their eyes around for other possible causes of the mishap. Perhaps, being countrymen, their eyes and senses were more acute than those of The Vale had been when their own trophy went missing. Perhaps the immediacy of events had sharpened those senses or perhaps it was the two holes in the plasterwork, peering like two accusing eyes which made the silhouette on the wall more noticeable. We may never know what it was that caused someone to shout, "They've nicked the ram's head!" but suddenly all eyes were focussed on the place where it was no longer hanging.

The Vale skipper was called upon to give an explanation or, more pertinently, to give it back. Now Wilf had been crafty enough not to inform the skipper of the plot so that he was innocent of any knowledge of it and he was able to calmly deflect the accusation, honestly declaring his ignorance of anything untoward. He pointed out that the theft could have occurred weeks or even months ago. He backed this up cleverly by relating what had happened at The Vale some years before when a trophy of theirs had been stolen, whilst all the time looking round for some sign of guilt amongst the home players. In all the circumstances he maintained that it was unfair and unfounded to accuse The Vale but it cut no ice; the allegation of theft was repeated more vehemently by the home side. It was then that the Vale skipper, who, although he was not quite sure, thought one of the home players had looked a bit uneasy when he was relating the theft of The Vale's trophy, felt he had to take a calculated gamble.

"Seeing as you have accused us openly, without any evidence," he said, "in the interests of clearing the air and maintaining our good relations, I must tell you that we have been informed by a reliable source that it was someone from your club who stole the trophy I mentioned earlier, from our club years ago and that since then you have hidden it away whenever we come here so that we might not have the chance of fairly recovering it. If you will give us our trophy back, if any of our lads has taken the ram's head I will see to it that it is given back to you and we will call it quits."

This was serious stuff and now eyes peered into eyes from both sides, searching for a guilty reaction. For a moment their skipper hesitated but then, his voice rising in anger, he said,

"But we haven't got your trophy and if we had we wouldn't be hiding it. That's a disgraceful accusation! We would not have expected that from The Vale. You're just trying to bluff your way out of it. You must give the ram's head back. Fair's fair: you've been caught in the act!"

These words brought a chorus of approval from the home side and things didn't look to be going The Vale's way but then one of the home players, not an official spokesman, it must be said, but an ill-disciplined, callow youth, blurted out,   "It wasn't your trophy anyway! I've seen the inscription on it! It belongs to Harlequins!"

This was tantamount to a murder suspect giving a cast-iron alibi and then saying it was self-defence anyway. It provoked a cry the equivalent of "Aha!" from the Vale lads and even the non-lawyers in the home side could see it hadn't done their case any good. Nevertheless, the argument continued ever more disagreeably and the Vale captain had to quell a minor scuffle by admonishing Gordon, an ex-paratrooper who always believed in taking the initiative in matters of self-defence,

"We don't want anything that isn't ours, Gordon. Give that man his shirt-front back."

Gordon complied, remarking that it must have been a cheap shirt anyway. It was like pouring oil on troubled waters then lighting it. Amongst the general abuse which followed from the home side there was one comment to which the Vale captain took a very strong exception and he announced,

"That's it! We will not stay here to be insulted whilst there is good ale to be had in the village," and he gave the order to drink up and leave.

The Vale contingent walked down into the town, expecting that they would find the coach waiting there. It wouldn't be difficult to find it as it was only a small town, in terms of population more of a village really. However, it was a quaint and picturesque little place with an open market square and a green which backed on to a fast-flowing salmon river. Such was its charm that it attracted a fair number of day-trippers. Consequently, it was endowed with a good choice of hostelries and when the lads arrived in the square they found themselves in the position of the prairie dog suddenly surrounded by several trees. They didn't know which one to go to first and so to make the most of this idyllic location they decided to split up into smaller groups, agreeing to meet back in the square in half an hour to compare notes and to decide where to go from there if, by then, the coach had not come back. In the meantime the captain and vice-captain took the responsibility to go and look for the missing transport.

Each of the pubs impressed its respective party of visitors and the original plan to meet up again was quickly abandoned. Instead one group sent out a messenger to tell the others they had found the best pub and they should all come there. But the messenger didn't come back. So they sent another. Then someone from another group came to say they had surely found the best pub so everybody should go there. The result was that each pub had its own hard core of resident aficionados whilst the remaining players were in a state of flux between the entire offering.

The town square itself provided an agreeable background in the evening sun. Tourists were an important source of revenue to the locals and communal efforts were made to keep the square neat, tidy and attractive. Nowadays daffodils are so ubiquitous we take them for granted but at that time those seemingly growing at random on the green were quite a novelty. Amongst the Vale lads was one who, following misdemeanours the previous week, had made a solemn and sincere promise to his loved one that he would be home in good time and in good order to take her out. Due to circumstances beyond his control – which he knew would not be an acceptable excuse – the way events were unfolding he felt his promise was already beginning to look rash and irredeemable. On seeing the daffodils in such abundance that a few would not be missed, and reasoning that as they were not in anyone's garden they must be considered wild flowers, he decided to equip himself with a peace offering.

He was spotted by a team-mate in transit from one pub to another. Surprised by this manifestation of a feminine side he had not previously known to exist in his colleague he went over to ask him what he was doing. On hearing the motive behind the sudden interest in springtime flora, he thought it seemed a sound idea. It was not long, therefore, before the incongruous sight of several rugby players industriously picking daffodils around the village square was to be observed. And it was, indeed, observed by a member of the local rate-paying gentry.

Now sportsmen tend by nature to be competitive. Appreciating that their generosity was unrestrained by the usual economic considerations and urged on by a desire to please or appease the loved one, there were some who sought to impress by acquiring the largest bunch. By the time the village bobby appeared on the scene the previously abundant display had been reduced to random faded specimens, forlorn sentinels to glories past.

In the tradition of exchanges between village policemen and suspected wrongdoers the constable opened with a simple, straightforward question to which he received an equally simple and straightforward answer. The obligatory formalities concluded the policeman went on to explain that the daffodils in question were not, in fact, wild flowers but that they had been cultivated by, and were the property of the town council. Now, as I may have mentioned already The Vale lads were an honest and law-abiding bunch and, having been appraised of their innocent mistake, they immediately and unanimously offered to rectify matters by giving the daffodils back. Although he initially appeared to be disarmed by this gesture of goodwill when the bobby noted, out of the corner of his eye, the presence of the villager who had made the complaint, it occurred to him that this might not be regarded as an entirely satisfactory outcome. He was moved to stamp his authority by the issue of a stern warning, not just to the daffodil pickers but to the complete Vale company which had, of course, by then assembled to see what was going on. The constable laid it on a bit thick - probably for the benefit of the ratepayer in the audience – and ultimately came to threaten that if there were any more problems all of The Vale lads would be "run" out of town". It is not within the ambit of these tales to delve into the workings of the human mind, let alone that of the average rugby player after he has consumed several pints but it could be that strains of Wilf's novel rendition of "High Noon" earlier in the evening to the accompaniment of a tin beer tray were still reverberating amongst the brain cells. Those strains might have been what influenced one of those present, on hearing the policeman's slightly off-beat turn of phrase, to spontaneously exclaim, "O.K.! Sheriff! Go for your gun!"

With the possible exception of the ratepayer, the constable, who lacked the assistance alcoholic refreshment can often bring to seeing the funny side of things, was the only one of those present who failed to collapse in laughter. Shortly afterwards there followed the second incongruous sight of the evening: a helmeted policeman shepherding a bunch of rugby players, who, of course, all agreed to go quietly, to the town boundary which, for the purpose, was deemed to be the verge of the trunk road which by-passed the town. It was not far away and the laughter had hardly subsided by the time they got there.

174

Nevertheless, above the racket, the policeman made audible his threat that anyone who came back into town would be locked up.

In the meantime the captain and vice-captain had been on something of a wild goose chase. They had found the only garage in the village was closed when they got there and there was no sign of the coach. By making enquiries they had eventually arrived at the garage owner's home some way out of the village. He told them that the coach had, indeed, been brought in but he had known immediately it was beyond him to effect a repair. The coach driver had gone off to the next decent-sized town some fifteen miles away to try his luck there but the garage owner was not optimistic about the outcome: "It's had it," he said.

The two had made their way back to the village square with the bad news but were puzzled to find not a single player in any of the pubs. Their confusion over this Marie Celestial situation was compounded when, on the conclusion of their pub to pub enquiries, they were spotted by the policeman who recognised their blazers and wanted to lock them up.

The skipper and his companion found it difficult to convince the constable that they had had no involvement in the episode which had led to the banishment of the other Vale players. The policeman only began to soften his stance when he remembered that the Chairman of the Bench was also the President of the local rugby club and he thought he would be wasting his time taking the matter forward. From past experience the Chairman's attitude - especially with rugby players – was, "Just lads having a bit of fun, no harm done and nobody hurt," and he would find a way of letting them off. In the end the policeman agreed to let the two of them go on condition that they joined the rest of the party and did not come back into town. Even if they, personally, had done nothing wrong, he said, he was not prepared to take the trouble of trying to distinguish them from the others. They could be a bit uncompromising once they got a bee in their bonnet up in that part of the world.

The somewhat chastened mood of the captain and vice-captain as they walked down to the main road contrasted sharply with that of the rest of the party. They could be heard from some way off, still celebrating with raucous laughter the incredible wit of the would-be gunslinger as the incident was re-lived several times. Of course, they would rather have been in the pubs in the village than by the side of the road but it was still a fine evening and the skipper would be along soon with the coach and there was always another pub not far away. However, the sight of the disconsolate pair walking down the road towards them soon put a dampener on proceedings and when they learnt about the coach it all went quiet for a while as they were forced to reassess the situation: the sun was beginning to set, they had no transport home, they couldn't go to the pub for a drink or even to the phone box to try to arrange alternative transport and they were miles from anywhere that was of any use to them. As the extent of their predicament sank in the gunslinger who so recently had been lauded and applauded for the spontaneity of his repartee found himself, edged by degrees from the centre to the periphery of the company where the odd sideways glance was cast in his direction and someone, forgetting his own contribution to the unfortunate situation, was heard to remark, only half in jest, "If only he had kept his big, silly mouth shut." He had gone from wit to twit in little longer than the time it takes the average prop-forward to tie his laces.

There was no shortage of solutions suggested but none of them was viable. One of the learned lawyers present stated his definite opinion that the constable had no authority to exclude any of them from the town but as he seemed unwilling himself to risk a night or two in the cells for the privilege of arguing the point before the magistrates the following Monday morning nobody else wanted to put it to the test either. Eventually, in sheer desperation rather than genuine hope one or two started trying to thumb a lift. Then an amazing thing happened: an empty coach came along and drew up. It did not belong to any firm with which The Vale had any association. The driver was not known to anyone there. I would have loved to have been able to say that he was a rugby player or that he had some association with the game but the truth is that he wasn´t and he didn't. He had just seen this group of lads obviously in a spot of bother and decided to stop. A lift to the next town would have been a good help but as it turned out he was going back to his base in the nearest large town to The Vale's clubhouse. In actual fact he dropped them off at the door and it cost them nothing more than a whip-round

So against all the odds The Vale first and third teams arrived back at the clubhouse at a reasonable hour but even then the surprises of the day were not over. Out of the blue you get one amazing coincidence then all of a sudden another one comes along. Earlier in the day the fourth team's opposition had cried off. They had been fortunate to get a game on the fixtures pool against a team The Vale had once used to play on a regular basis but had not played for several years. After the game the Vale lads had been astonished to see the cherished Vale trophy as bold as brass on the clubhouse wall. Although the deed was greatly elaborated upon in years to come the plain facts were that the trophy had been displayed in an easily accessible position and it was in a fast car on its way back to The Vale before the first pints of the evening had worked their way through.

When the skipper saw the trophy on the bar as he came into the clubhouse where it was flanked by several fourth team players in an advanced state of celebration, he did not know whether to laugh or cry. He was overjoyed to see the trophy back but dismayed when he thought of the mayhem which had been caused to relations with Lunesdale. For once The Vale had been in the wrong. He immediately took Wilf to one side.

"Wilf, we must give them their ram's head trophy back."

"But, skip ..."

"I'm not having any argument, Wilf. Hand it over and I'll see it gets back somehow."

"But I can't, skip. I haven't got it."."

"Don't mess about. You personally might not have it but I'm sure you know where it is."

"That's the problem; Jimmy had it last."

"I don't see how that's a problem," said the skipper although a slight change in his expression when he heard Jimmy's name mentioned told a different story.

"What do you mean – he had it *last?*"

Wilf could see that a full account was required. He went through the sequence of events which culminated with Jimmy, the fly-half, running out into the car park at Lunesdale and hiding the ram's head. He went on,

"When we left their clubhouse we still thought they had got our trophy so Jimmy managed to pick up the ram's head from where he had hid it and put it in his kit bag. When we went down to the village we were all carrying our bags with us because ..."

"I'm with you so far, Wilf. Because we couldn't put them on the coach. Can you get to the point?"

"Well, I don't really want to have to tell you this, skip, but Jimmy had his bag with him whilst he was picking the daffodils and when he saw the bobby coming he panicked. For once, he didn't want to be caught in possession so he dropped the ram's head over the wall into the river[62]."

---

[62] *That was the original ram's head; the one currently on display is the seventh replacement.*

Rugby League Country

We don't play for adoration
We don't play for victory
We just play for recreation
Merry, merry men are we
Balls to Harlequins
Balls to Harlequins
We won't play you any more
We won't play you any more.
                    (To the tune of Cwm Rhondda)

Although instances of bull baiting were still being recorded in the United Kingdom in 1878 it had been banned by Parliament along with bear baiting and dog and cock fighting in 1835. Thanks to William Webb Ellis, Rugby Football came along to fill the vacuum. In the nineteenth century rugby was at its most popular in Lancashire and Yorkshire where it was not organised along class lines; numbered amongst the players were mill and factory workers who worked shifts over a six day week. At The Vale in my playing days we also had players drawn from all walks of life; for example, three were milkmen. There was a plasterer, a plumber a joiner, a farmer and a master baker. All the rest were solicitors.

The laws[63] of The Rugby Football Union founded in 1871 provided that the game should be played by amateurs only. The difficulty the Northern clubs had at that time was that if shift-workers did not complete the number of full shifts per week which their terms of employment required, they could be disproportionately penalised in their pay packets. Consequently, some clubs wanted to compensate their players for "broken-time" as it was difficult to argue for the fairness of a system which resulted in amateur players suffering a heavy financial loss for taking time off to play whilst the clubs they were playing for were often collecting substantial gate money. At the

---

[63] *They were called "laws" because they were drawn up by solicitors.*

same time there were some rugby clubs run by mill owners who did not deduct any pay at all from their employees who left work early to play. Arguably, this was a form of indirect payment for playing which provided an incentive for players to join those clubs where this arrangement was in force. The Northerners thought that legitimising and regulating such compensatory payments was the best way to combat "shamateurism" or "veiled professionalism" as it was then called whilst the Southerners said they thought it would be the thin end of the wedge if payments were openly allowed (which led the Northerners to think the Southerners were happy for illicit payments to continue to be made as long as they were kept quiet). The difference of opinion culminated in the foremost Northern Clubs jumping before they were pushed; they left the Rugby Football Union and formed the Northern Union, the forerunner of the Rugby League at a meeting at The George Hotel in Huddersfield on 28th August 1895. Just a day or two short of a century later history repeated itself but this time Rugby Union as a whole became "open" to professional players. The slow-burning fuse lit by the Australian Dispensation Law in 1967 had finally reached its destination.

The immediate consequences of the 1895 schism had been plain to see: the Northern Union soon moved to fully embrace professionalism; the Rugby League was born and quickly took over from Union as the most popular form of the game; the number of clubs affiliated to the RFU halved, almost wiping out Union in the North of England and the England national team which had won the Triple Crown in 1892, with a total of eleven players from Lancashire and Yorkshire in the side, did not win the Four Nations again for eighteen years, the longest gap in its history. The split is usually described as "acrimonious": something of a euphemism. Pettiness and hypocrisy prevailed as Union claimed the high moral ground. Even the faces of players, who had helped England win the Championship but subsequently turned to League, were blanked out on team photographs hung at Twickenham.

Neither Union nor League a hundred years ago was played to the same rules as they are today. Who pays the piper calls the tune and over the years League made a series of changes – the lineout was abolished as early as 1897 - with the aim of making the game more entertaining for the paying spectators, whose interests became paramount. The higher echelons of rugby union are currently grappling with the same problem but the mere mortals, whilst they must endure the continual tinkering of the rule-makers, are still free to play the game purely for their own enjoyment. They can still say, "We'll play how we want," and, "Sod the spectators!" even if there aren't any. There are still places in the team for both the short and squat and the long and gangly. Long may it continue. Long live the mere mortals!

The antipathy between Union and League may be becoming a thing of the past now that both disciplines openly pursue the common goal of making money. Rugby League continues to be a two-dimensional war of attrition – collisions and kicks - whilst Rugby Union twists one way and then another, trying to avoid arriving at the same destination whilst providing the kind of non-stop, bish- bash action which the customers are deemed to demand. One good thing to come out of this new season / new rules regime is that it has got me out of the futile habit of shouting at the television over refereeing decisions at the breakdown or the tight scrum as I have, painfully, come to realise that I am now probably just about as clueless as those I used to despise for wasting space at Twickenham. My self-esteem is only partially restored when I hear them singing "Swing low sweet chariot" and I can smirk at their ignorance. I cannot believe they know what an obscene parody of the Negro spiritual the traditional rugby version is in its "hands only" form. (I still think it would be great to see it done at Twickenham instead of a Mexican wave during a particularly boring passage of play though. Dream on! But perhaps even better still would be to witness some self-important drummer boy at a Heineken or Premier League match being escorted towards an early exit wearing his instrument).

However, when these tales began the schism caused by the disagreement over broken time was still very much a live issue.

In common with their contemporaries at other local clubs all The Vale lads were fully versed in every historic detail of the original controversy and the questions it continued to raise, even those of a hypothetical nature. For example, would League have gone to 13 men if they had thought of allowing lifting in the lineout? This and hundreds of similar questions pertaining to the whole range of connected issues were a continual source of fascination for the Vale lads. Naturally, no better opportunity for an in depth discussion came along than on the coach to a game against a team which might be considered to be influenced by rugby league culture. On one such away coach – on the outward journey, of course, - the conversation ran along the following lines:

"Who are we playing today?" asked Jim who either never bothered to look at any other detail on his selection card other than the meeting time or, if he did, could never remember it come Saturday.

"You'll be pleased to hear it's Fortsallians, Jim."

"Yes. It's those dirty bastards again," Pablo interjected.

"In that case where are we going to stop on the way back, then?" asked Jim. "I fancy some proper pie and peas at The Waggon."

"Why? Don't we get fed there?" Tony, a younger player, having the pleasure of his first visit to Fortsallians, asked anxiously.

"We do but it's pie and baked beans ," Jim replied. "Never hits the spot somehow. Poor combination. Nothing like pie and peas."

To be fair it wasn't just in rugby league country that pies were served with baked beans; they seemed to be standard fodder all round Manchester and the suburbs. The Vale lads used to think that it was because it was too easy for city folk just to open a can of beans whereas peas had to be put in to steep the night before, then somebody had to watch over the cooking of them – a ham shank thrown in for flavour - to see that they arrived at that glorious mushy consistency – not too firm, not too soft – just at the right time. Then there were the little things which made all the difference: the pickled red cabbage, the sliced onions and mint sauce. All these things were very important to Jim. Not everybody placed the same importance on the after-match fare as he did but, disregarding the after-match fodder, The Vale never really looked forward to playing against clubs where attitudes were considered to be influenced by the professional league clubs nearby; they were wary of the win at all costs mentality which playing for money was thought to encourage and which, in turn, tended to lead to dirty play. In those days, when League was televised, there were plenty of stiff arms, clothes lines, short arm slogs and the like to be seen and Eddie Waring seemed to revel in commentating on the rough stuff. On the other hand, The Vale, with one or two notable exceptions over the years, subscribed to the theory that they were in it to win it by playing generally in accordance with the rules and they liked to play against clubs who were similarly aware of the need to be able to go to work on Monday morning. That is not to say that both sides were expected to play by all the rules all the time and were horrified by any transgression. It came to down to a question of the degree of respect for the rules, the most important of which were those regarding foul play, in particular, late and high tackles. In the final analysis it is the referee's opinion on the day which officially determines whether a tackle is late or high but referees are guided by their governing bodies. At one time a tackle above the waist in open play might have been considered high in Union whilst at the same time in League anything above the eyebrows was frowned upon. Over the years the two codes have converged and seem to have hit a compromise at anything on or above the chin.

In the interests of self-preservation, however, it is imperative not to let matters rest entirely with the match official; indispensable though the referee's opinion may be it is always prudent to take the actual rules of engagement into account as well as the official ones. It is all very well the team being awarded a penalty but it is difficult to exhibit a high level of enthusiasm, even if a score results whilst you, personally, are on the deck being treated for concussion. With this in mind the mid-week training at The Vale prior to a match in Rugby League Country would consist solely of practising running round as fast as you could with your chin pressed tightly to your chest. On the Saturday when the opposition came out you could tell they obviously followed the same routine but they had been doing it since childhood as they no longer had any necks and their heads turned with their shoulders.

Unfortunately, once you had been lumbered with a fixture you did not like it was not easy to get rid of it however much you would have liked to sing 'Balls to Fortsallians' and have done with it. By convention 'dropping' a fixture only occurred either at the instigation of the victors after a series of one-sided games or after unacceptably violent confrontations. Occasionally, the RFU came to the rescue: I remember that one club in or near Manchester, where an extreme culture of thuggery had taken hold, being banned as a result of one of their players having been found taking to the field with threepenny bits[64] taped to his knuckles.

Even more than usual, the referee's role was highly important in such games, the task could be a difficult one and some referees were not up to it. The ability or otherwise of referees was another frequent topic of conversation on the away coach and Pablo's earlier interjection of "dirty bastards" had brought his presence to the attention of another player who was not a big fan of his style of play.

"That's a bit rich coming from you, Pablo! Anyway, how come you're playing today? I thought you got sent off last week."

"It was all a misunderstanding ..." Pablo began but was interrupted by Jim.

"You can say that again! And there will be plenty more misunderstandings if he carries on the same way."

"Why? What happened?"

Jim continued, "For the second lineout running Pablo slipped his arm inside their jumper's arm[65]. Unfortunately, their chap didn't

---

[64] *This was a small dodecagonal – OK, twelve-sided coin – measuring 21mm in diameter and 2.5mm thick worth three old pennies. It was introduced in 1937 and discontinued on decimalisation in 1971.*

[65] *At that time the laws did not provide for a clear space between the two sets of forwards at the lineout.*

understand Pablo was just trying to be friendly; he thought he was trying to hold his arm down so he couldn't jump for the ball."

"Why should he have thought that, I wonder?"

"Exactly, but that's just how these misunderstandings come about. Anyway their chap took exception to it and Pablo took exception to him taking exception and they ended up having a non-verbal debate about it long after the ball had gone. The ref blew but Pablo carried on so he got sent off."

"No. No. No! That's not it at all," said Pablo. "I didn't get sent off for fighting."

"That's what I heard."

"No. No. The ref blew but the other bloke wanted to carry on so, obviously, I had to pacify him. That didn't please the ref so he gave us both a lecture. He said, 'You should have stopped when I blewed my whistle'. I said, 'You *blewed* your whistle. You can't say that. You mean you *blew* your whistle. A referee should know better."

"So he sent you off?"

"Yes. He was out of order, of course, but he did."

"That'll teach you, clever bugger. So how come you're playing this week?"

"He said afterwards he wasn't going to report me. I suppose he didn't want to have show himself up before the disciplinary committee."

"You jammy sod!"

"That shouldn't come into it really though," said Gordon who had no real issues with Pablo's robust style of play but found his presumed intellectual superiority difficult to stomach. "It wouldn't matter if a ref was illiterate as long as he could do the job properly."

"What? Would that mean even prop forwards could be allowed to ref?" Pablo asked, looking artificially incredulous.

"Why not?" replied Gordon, fired up. "At least they'd know what was going on in the scrum. They'd know all about that. That would be a good start. Most refs haven't the first clue what goes on in the front row. Nobody has a clue unless they've played there."

"It would never work," said Pablo.

"Why not? Are you saying a prop wouldn't be fit enough to keep up?" Gordon who was a very fit and mobile prop, asked aggressively.

"No. Not necessarily," said Pablo realising he wouldn't win the argument down that route.

"What are you saying then? Wouldn't be bright enough?" Gordon asked even more aggressively.

"No. It's a Catch 22 situation."

"What d'you mean a Catch 22 situation? All the same you teachers. You have to talk in bloody riddles."

"I mean, yes, I agree that a prop forward would know what's going on in the scrum but if he did see anything he'd never blow up for it because he'd think it had nothing to do with the ref."

Although Gordon seemed to hesitate for a moment he had imbibed the culture of wit and repartee at The Vale for too long to be found wanting for a telling riposte.

"Pablo," he said, smiling, and then paused for effect, "why don't you fuck off."

At that moment a veteran came down the aisle to join in the conversation. "Pablo getting sent off reminds me of something that happened some years ago when we were here? Do you remember, Gordon? That time we thought Piggy was going to get banned?"

"Not likely to forget it, am I?" Gordon said.

"Why? What happened there then?" Tony, the new lad, wanted to know.

"Well, there had been some rough stuff on the last couple of occasions we'd played them so the forwards decided they'd have a plan in case it all kicked off again. It was their hooker who always seemed to start it all. The idea was that on the signal our front row would leave room for Badger to swing through from the second row and give him one. Anyway the ref was useless, he had no idea what was going on in the front row and it did start. So the signal was given and at the next scrum there was this almighty crack and the scrum collapsed. When we got up there was poor old Gordon out cold."

"What? You mean our Gordon?"

186

"That's right. It was a cracking punch but Badger hit the wrong man. Of course, the ref thought they'd done it, awarded a penalty and gave them a warning. They knew they hadn't done it and started talking back so the ref gave another ten yards. We kicked the penalty which didn't please them, of course, but, obviously, they had sussed out what we were up to as well. Then, when Gordon came round, he wasn't too happy about being laid out either. It was more frustration than anything. For a start he'd always thought it was more blessed to give than receive but if he did take a punch he didn't mind so much as long as he could give a couple back. Obviously, he wasn't going to hit his own man but he'd got his mind set on taking it out on somebody the next chance he got. Not long after that a scrum broke up in a brawl. The ref had completely lost control by then but somehow he ended up in the middle of it, trying to stop one of our guys from punching somebody, I think. Anyway, Piggy came running up, saw this arse in white shorts sticking out and stuck the boot in. Anyway it turned out the ref was wearing the same shorts as them and it was his arse he kicked."

"Bloody hell! He kicked the ref?"

"Right up the arse. And the thing was the ref knew who'd done it because Piggy was all set to give him another one when he managed to get a look round."

"That doesn't sound like Piggy."

"No. But it was that sort of game. There'd been all sorts of things going on right from the start."

"So then what happened?"

"Well, everybody stopped fighting and Piggy apologised. Said he hadn't meant to kick the ref and he looked more shocked than anybody. But he couldn't deny he had meant to kick somebody."

"So he got sent off then?"

"We all thought he would and that he'd get banned. But it turned out he wasn't a proper ref; he was one of theirs. They said the Society ref hadn't turned up but I bet they never asked for one. Bloody shower. They hadn't bothered telling us it wasn't a neutral ref, of course. Anyway to give the ref his due he admitted he'd lost control and that it was partly his fault. He said both sides would have to calm it down and have a bit of sense or he would call the game off. If we wanted a game of rugby it was up to us. If we just wanted a fight he'd leave us to it. So the captains had a talk and everybody settled down after that. Gordon thought it was a shame because he was sure we'd have licked them at fighting, didn't you Gordon?"

"We would definitely have had a much better chance of winning at fighting seeing how you were playing", Gordon replied.

"So Piggy got away with it then?"

"I suppose you could say that but with the ref not being an official one and what's more, not neutral and we hadn't been told about it they couldn't have taken it any further anyway. You tend to get that kind of thing over here; they just don't respect the rules the same."

As the Vale lads trotted out on to the pitch they saw two men in uniform standing near the touchline. The uniforms were black with white waist and shoulder belts and a peaked cap. One of the uniforms looked very new.

"Bloody hell! It's the St John's Ambulance with a trainee, like a pair of vultures, hoping for someone to practise on."

"They've even got a stretcher lined up. That's all we need."

"That's a point. Do we have a stretcher at The Vale? I've never seen it."

"They keep it in the referee's room."

"Best place for it: out of sight, out of mind."

"It wouldn't be so bad but they never seem to know what to do if it comes to anything beyond a sticking plaster."

"Still, they are volunteers. You never know when you might need them and they've got to practise on somebody."

"It's just a bad omen. That's all. They never seem to go away empty-handed."

As it turned out one of The Vale lads did get injured. It didn't have anything to do with the Rugby League influence or the presence of the vultures; it was just one of those things. He hurt his shoulder going into a tackle. Although the St. John's men had more in their armoury than the magic sponge there wasn't anything they could do to patch him up. They thought it was either a dislocated shoulder or a broken collar bone. In any event the player was unable to continue and had to go off. His early exit was applauded by both sides as he was helped off by the ambulancemen and as he left the field one of his team-mates shouted some helpful advice:-

"Have a shower. Don't run the bath or there'll be no hot water for the rest of us!"

After the game The Vale found the injured player at the bar. The St. John's had had a field day. He was bandaged right up to the neck and his non-drinking arm was in a sling.

"I told you about that lot. All they come for is some bandaging practice."

"Can I have some of those bandages after?" asked Jim. "I could do with some new tie-ups."

"What's the damage?"

"They don't know exactly... "

"Told you."

"They said I need to go to casualty for an X-ray."

"I knew it! We never get away from this place without going to casualty. At least we know where it is by now."

"It'll be like Piccadilly Station. It always is on a Saturday afternoon."

"Well, he can't help it, can he?"

"How bad is it? Anything broken?" asked the skipper.

"Not sure. It's not so bad now I've had a couple of pints."

"We'd better go just in case. It won't be any better at The General by the time we get back. The queue will probably be worse with all the Saturday drunks. We'll just have a couple of swift ones here to show willing. There's a pub just down the road from the hospital with a chippy next door so we can drop the rabble off there."

"I've been there before; it's a bit of a dive!"

"A step up from your usual haunts if it's only a bit of a dive."

"Sod off!"

As had been predicted the local casualty department was doing a roaring trade with all the sports injuries and there was a long wait. It was always the X-Rays which seemed to cause the biggest delay. A couple of hours later the captain and the injured player returned to find the rest of the party in the pub and to give them the good news that nothing was broken, just bad bruising. Meanwhile the ale had been going down well.

"Come on, lads," said the skipper after quickly downing a pint. "We need to be off. We said we weren't going to be late back this week."

But they were still only in the outskirts of the city when the chorus began from the back of the bus:-

"Does the driver want a wee wee
Does the driver want a wee wee
Does the driver want a wee wee
' Cos the dirty bastards at the back are pissing on the floor. "

"That's it. We're on the slippery slope now." Jim said to Tony.

"How do you mean?"

"Well the coach isn't booked out late tonight so the driver'll want to get back but if they keep this up he'll get worried they really are pissing on the floor so he'll give in and they'll get a piss-stop. And where will that be? At a pub, of course. So it'll be half a pint out and a pint in so in another ten minutes they'll be wanting to stop again. In the end we won't be able to get past a pub without stopping."

"Shit!" said Tony. "I hadn't reckoned on that."

"Why? You're not bothered are you? It'll be a good night."

"Well, it's just that..."

"You haven't got a promise on have you? Hey, lads, Tony's got a promise on!"

"Who with? It's not that bird you were chatting up at the disco last week is it, you sly get?"

"I'm saying nothing."

"You haven't arranged to meet her down at the club, have you? You shouldn't have done that."

"Serious mistake!"

"Don't worry, lad, there's only one of our blokes who would try to pinch another bloke's bird and he's on the bus with us. Aren't you, Pablo?"

"Sod off!"

"What do you reckon, lads? Are we going to try to get back to the club so we can have a look at this bird he's got?"

"What's she like? Is she fit?"

"She'd be out of your class anyway."

" You can talk. What about that rough looking bird you ended up with last week? Still, she did look like she'd shag till the cows came home though."

"You would know all about cows and shagging. Hey! At least, not like someone else we know, spotted sneaking out of dirty Doreen's at six o'clock on Sunday morning, before it got light, hoping nobody'd see him."

"Which dirty bugger was that?"

"Tell 'em, Taffy."

"Well, I'm not going to mention any names but he's sitting next to Bill."

"You Welsh wazzock, Taffy. I thought we'd agreed you'd keep your mouth shut if I did the same."

"Why was Taffy there as well? Good lad Taffy!"

"He had his best wellies on too."

"He's lying. He knows I was there for purely professional reasons when I spotted him coming out."

"Whose profession? Not yours. Hers more likely."

"Hey! Taff's going up in the world; he's not just a milkman any more; he's a professional purveyor of liquid dairy produce."

"Sounds like milk's not the only liquid he's purveying!"

There was a chorus of "Dirty bugger!"

"Taffy was just about to sneak in as I was coming out. He tried to say he was delivering the milk but he didn't have a bottle in his hand."

"That was because I'd already put it down on the step, you prat."

Another chorus of jeers.

"Hey, I say good for Taffy! At least Doreen's better looking than the sheep up on Whiteley Moor."

"That's a matter of opinion."

" Come to think about it I've seen Taffy's float many a time down that street."

"Obviously.That's because I deliver the milk down there."

"Sounds like that's not all you're delivering."

"Anyway how do you know which street it is, you dirty bugger?"

Amongst more jeers the coach drew to a halt.

"Hey up, lads! Here we are: piss stop."

"Flippin' eck! The Rose and Crown; we are seeing some rough shops tonight."

"Anyone'd think you're used to a better class of hostelry."

"The way we're going we'll end up in The Nag's Head yet."

"That is a real dive!"

"You would know."

Consumption rates were beginning to spread out as the night drew on. Those first to finish their pints thought they had time for another whilst the slower ones caught up but they were still drinking their second pints when they slower ones had finished so they, in turn, thought they might as well have another pint whilst they were waiting and so on. It was quite some time before everybody got back into synchronisation and the coach could set off again. As Jim had predicted it was not long before the refrain the driver dreaded was being taken up again:-

"Does the driver want a wee wee,

Does the driver want a wee wee ..."

The driver wasn't a bad bloke. It wasn't known whether he volunteered or whether he had worse luck with the short straw than the other drivers who worked for the bus company but he seemed to draw The Vale quite regularly. He didn't drink but as the evening wore on he seemed to catch the mood of the rest of the party and he developed a disrespect for the Highway Code which would have alarmed the passengers had they not been pissed. It earned him the nickname of Jacky Ickx[66].The bus company only paid him for the hours the coach was booked out for but he didn't seem to bother. On this occasion it was apparent that any hope of returning at a reasonable hour had evaporated. Realising this, the skipper organised a whip-round for the driver whilst sufficient funds still remained available to match the natural generosity of the passengers.

Tony protested at the projected late return for the sake of being able to say he had done so but resigned himself to the fate of his date and the way was cleared for the next stop.

"Pub on the left, Jacky! Hundred yards," shouted the look-out.

The Vale lads disembarked with an even split between those heading for the bar and the toilets.

"Hey! This is an old pub! They've still got the stones outside!"

"Yeah. Not many left now. They're all getting modernised."

"You know, I prefer to go outside for a leak. It's more natural somehow."

"It's not just that: you go outside now and again and you get a breath of fresh air and ..."

"Not here you don't! It's humming like a hive of bees."

"Well, it is actually. It's rank in here but I didn't just mean in the nook itself. You can get a breath of air on your way here. Out of

---

[66] *The Belgian Formula 1 racing driver in the 60s and 70s famous for wins at The Nurburgring and also for a record six victories at the Le Mans 24 hour race.*

the smoke for a while. Clears your head and you can tell how pissed you're getting."

"Too late for some of that lot in there; they've gone. Have you seen the state of Philip?"

"Well, he walloped a few quick ones down after he got injured and it's caught up with him. At least he'll be feeling no pain."

"Till tomorrow."

"Have you noticed it's always just the gents that's outside? Never the ladies. And they're always going on about this equality business."

"Well, I don't reckon it would be a good idea to have the ladies' outside at this place."

"I know what you mean. It's even rougher than that last place we were in. What's it called?"

"Don't know. Bill'll know. Bill! What's this place called?"

"It's the Nags Head."

"The Nags Head? Bloody hell. Wasn't there some tale about this place years ago? The lads won a load of money on the horses with tips they got off an old jockey in here and ended up having a big piss-up?"

"Piss-up's right; in more ways than one. Somebody's car ran out of petrol and they ended up in here. It doesn't look like the place's changed much. 'Team Spirit' was the name of the horse. I remember that. It won at some ridiculous odds and for some reason they had to come back here to collect their winnings. A fortune, it was, but they spent it all on ale. They even ended up losing a bet with some woman about how high they could piss up a wall."

"Hell fire! How did they manage to do that?"

"I don't know the full story. It was a long time ago. There was something about they didn't check the rules properly beforehand and in the end they couldn't use their hands or something like that. The woman was an old pro and she won easily."

"That's right. I remember something about it now. There was something about the woman having big tits but she skenned like a bag of whelks."

"A bit like her over there you reckon?"

" Bloody hell! I see what you mean."

"What was that about big tits?"

"Here he is. Say the magic words and Pablo appears out of nowhere."

"That bird over there. Just your type. Basically sound but rough round the edges. Just the way you like 'em."

"She's not that bad. Better than that one you ended up taking home last week, you drunken bum."

"What do you mean? She was a nice girl."

"Yeah. After fifteen pints."

Pablo deemed it important that the lady should make his acquaintance and made his way over to give her the opportunity.

"He'll worry rats, that bugger."

"He'll be back soon enough. He won't want to pay for it."

Sure enough he wasn't gone long but when he came back he brought the lady with him.

"Hey lads, listen to this! This lass has a proposition to make."

"Not tonight, thank you."

"No listen. It's not that. It's not what you're thinking."

"Go on. Try us. It wouldn't be anything to do with pissing up a wall, would it?"

"How the hell did you know?"

"It's all been done before. Some of the lads fell for the trick here years and years ago."

"It couldn't have been me then," said the young lady. "I'm not that old, am I?"

"No. Point taken. But there are a number of similarities in the description."

"It could've been my mother, I suppose."

"Anyway, it'll be the same trick. We can't use our hands so we get stung for the bet."

"There's no rule says you can't use your hands. We just have to agree the rules beforehand. I'm not bothered as long as it's the same for both sides. It's up to you."

195

Pablo drew the others to one side.

"I don't see how we can lose ..."

"Less of the 'we' – excuse the pun."

"No. It's obvious," said Pablo. "I see it now. She was going to pull a scam on us but now she's been rumbled she can't really back out without admitting it so she's betting we won't call her bluff. I can't see how we can lose if we can use our hands."

"Your reasoning's very sound. I'll hold your coat if you want," offered Gordon.

"You mean you're not coming in on it?"

"Exactly. You're on your own."

"You set of bloody chickens! Anyway I'm not having it said that The Vale shirked a challenge from a woman."

Shortly afterwards the stage with which the reader, unlike the current Vale protagonist, is already familiar, was again set down in the yard at the back adjacent to the gents. Some chalk was once again borrowed from the dartboard and a line was drawn parallel to the backyard wall. The gentleman from The Vale agreed, of course, that the lady should have first go. She squatted down delicately and, having removed her knickers earlier, lifted her skirt at the back. Then, whilst bending over, under the cover of her skirt at the front, she manipulated her fingers to such effect that a jet of urine was observed to pass over the full height of the wall with sufficient force to dislodge the helmet of a passing policeman . (Had there been one which, I'm sorry to have to admit, in the interests maintaining a true account, that there wasn't). But that detail did not affect the final score: -
Nags Head Ladies 2 The Vale 0. (Over two legs).

Vickers Away

Pablo would have had to take a seat had he not already been anticipating the arrival of a bacon butty at the breakfast table. The card he was looking at seemed to say 'Vickers Away'. 'Vickers - Away?' He was sure that couldn't be right. Where the hell had he put his glasses?

On Monday evenings The Vale's selection committee met at the clubhouse to choose the teams for the coming Saturday's fixtures. The committee consisted of the club chairman, each of the team captains and Roy, the team secretary, who brought with him a stack of pre-printed postcards. Roy filled in the blanks on these cards as the meeting progressed. He ran his own little production line and by the time the meeting came to a close all the cards were neatly filled in, stamped, addressed and ready for posting. He would drop them off in the postbox on his way home after the meeting. Those selected would receive their cards first post[67] Wednesday morning. Pablo was one of the chosen and the card he had received read:-

YOU HAVE BEEN SELECTED TO PLAY FOR THE ~~FIRST~~ / A / ~~EXTRA A / B~~ XV AGAINST
Vickers   ~~AT HOME~~ / AWAY
MEET AT THE CLUBHOUSE AT *10.00* **AM**

Pablo found his glasses and read again the dreaded words "Vickers Away". He had been selected for the 'A' team which was bad enough at the best of times for Pablo was a natural first team

---

[67] *First post: The Post office used to make two deliveries of mail on weekdays in urban areas. When first and second class postage was introduced in 1968 mail stamped first class was supposed to arrive on the first post which generally arrived before people went to work.*

player. But Vickers *Away*? Surely not? 'Vickers Away' were just two little words and looking at them you would not have realised the power for good or ill which they contained. Not everyone's reaction was the same as Pablo's; down the valley, Jim, who rarely looked at his fixture list once the season had started, was pleasantly surprised when he read his card. Not only had he been promoted to the second team but he could also look forward to a full day out. Playing away at Vickers always meant a stay to the death; he liked the ale up there (to be truthful there was hardly anywhere where he didn't find something commendable about the ale), and he was sure to be in the good company of like-minded souls.

Elsewhere the reaction was similarly mixed; 'Vickers Away' was bad news for grandparental life expectancy. Two or three were bound to find their number had come up that week; it was the same every year. (Pablo thought of that one but he knew Roy was a crafty operator and it was rumoured he kept a list. Pablo had already used his four up so he wouldn't be able to get away with it again). There were others like Jim for whom the arrival of the Wednesday morning card meant that they had a little extra to look forward to at the weekend whilst, on the other hand, at some of its destinations those two little words would act as a catalyst for niggling injuries which could wait no longer to be rested, for jobs around the house which became emergencies and for visits to in-laws which, reluctantly, could no longer be postponed.

The first team captain knew full well the havoc that "Vickers Away" could cause with team selection. This time the problem would not directly concern his team as they would be playing Vickers at home. He was, however, the club captain as well as team captain and took his responsibilities in that direction seriously. Besides, he had for some time been unhappy with the fitness levels of one or two of his regular players and he did not consider it a coincidence that they were the ones rarely seen at training sessions. Matters had been brought to a head during last week's game when a try had been missed as a consequence of one player's lack of fitness: a back row forward[68] who had been unable to keep up with play in the later stages of the game had tried to join in the back line, fumbled a ball he had no business going for and cost them a certain score. He was minded to hand out a lesson and he had realised the away game at Vickers would provide him with the ideal opportunity. Craftily, after the game he had laid more emphasis than usual on asking each player about his availability for the following week and he had ensured he was seen to be making notes in a little book. He knew that "Vickers Away" could have amazing effects on the memory; it had been known to encourage the sudden recollection on a Wednesday morning that a sibling's wedding[69] was taking place that Saturday, an event which had completely slipped the mind the player's mind only four days earlier. This time the skipper was determined not to allow any easy opportunity to slip the hook. Excuses would have to be either cast iron or completely original and, preferably, both. He knew he could rely on Roy, the team secretary, to sift them out.

Vickers, as befitted the works team of a large public limited company, had good pitches and well-maintained changing facilities. Any of their teams was difficult to beat and represented a strong but fair challenge to The Vale. They put on a good tea after the game, the ale wasn't bad once you got used to it and it was sold at W.M.C. prices[70]. The home players were a good bunch of lads, most of whom stayed on to drink with the Vale lads after the game. They also put on

---

[68] *Back row forwards used to have a bad habit of turning up in the threequarter line and ruining moves. Nowadays, when leading players are so much fitter, it is the front row forwards who do it.*
[69] *Weddings then, almost without exception, took place on a Saturday especially if they were held in a church.*
[70] *Working Men's Clubs, being non-profit making, were usually a few pence a pint cheaper than the pubs. We are talking old pence here, the currency not being decimalised until 1971. You could still get a pint of bitter for less than two shillings (10p) in some places.*

a disco in the clubhouse which was well attended by the young ladies who worked for the company. There would be at least one of The Vale lads upon whose memory was permanently etched with striking it lucky the previous year and who hoped that neither a year's absence nor the lack of any intervening communication [71] would have altered true love's course or, alternatively, that lightning might, indeed, strike twice. That was the positive side. On the negative side the journey was a tedious one which involved passing through more than one traffic bottleneck in Lancashire and Cumberland before reaching the winding road which threaded its way through the Furness peninsula to Barrow. It was necessary to allow at least three and a half hours for the journey and some breathing space at the other end. This required departure at an hour regarded by many a younger player as indecently close to dawn for a Saturday morning and there were plenty who found it difficult to perform well in the game after such a journey; early scores could easily be conceded which made winning even more difficult. The deciding factor was the inevitable late stay; personal circumstances decided for each individual whether this was a blessing or a curse; where one might look forward to a good night on the ale another might worry about the hangover and where one might see a new romantic opportunity another might see a difficulty with an existing relationship.

If some Vale players travelled with reluctance the same considerations applied to the Vickers players and no doubt being carded "The Vale Away" gave rise to similar team selection problems. Some would have to put in an extra shift at the shipyard on Saturday morning, "Foreman says we've got to finish this aircraft carrier by Easter," or take the dog to the vet's. "Sorry, can't do it any other time than Saturday morning."

---

[71] *If there was no phone what could you do? Most Vale players subscribed to the belief "Do right and fear no man. Don't write and fear no woman".*

Of course, they would still be available to play at home. This meant that if you were playing for either Vale second or fourth teams, who partnered each other on away games, you could expect to be ambushed at Vickers; their second team would be reinforced by a number of regular first teamers unable to make the journey away and their fourths by regular third teamers. One sided rugby matches are not a lot of fun if it's your team behind the posts all afternoon.

Inevitably, it was the fourths (or B team) which bore the brunt of all the cry-offs for the buck could pass no further. The fourth team selected on Monday evening would contain fifteen names but it became depleted as the week went on as some originally selected for the third team were promoted to fill in for cry-offs in the second team and they in turn were replaced by fourth team selections. To the partial rescue came the Vickers specialists. These were the guys who, for one reason or another, might not be able to play regularly all season but they made sure the team secretary knew they were always available for Vickers Away.

The team secretary's high level of organisation has already been noted. He had taken the precaution of carding five extra for the B team to compensate for the cry-offs he knew he was going to get: some would be genuine and some would just be trying to pull the wool over his eyes. Nevertheless, although he had spent a large part of Friday afternoon on the telephone cajoling and threatening he had exhausted the list of reserves including all the Vickers specialists and he had still come up short. He had telephoned the fourth team captain to tell him of the situation and he had made some desperate phone calls of his own.

Despite all these efforts still only ten were expected to turn up for definite with two or three promising to do their best. By 10.15 on Saturday morning, however, none of these bests had materialised into a physical appearance. The "A" team had fifteen so the full party comprised twenty five. The coach was preparing to leave. Just then, rounding the corner into the club car park at speed, came a battered old pick-up. As the driver hastily emerged the door swung off its bottom hinge as it was accustomed to do if not treated with due care.

"Bloody hell! It's Bones!"

"It can't be; he retired years ago."

"No. He's just coming back from injury and taking his time about it."

"He's always coming back from somewhere. Half the time before he's got there."

"It's got to be him. It couldn't be anyone else. Look at the state of that pick-up."

It was, indeed, Bones: 'B' for Bradley Ownsworth to give him his full name, a man who had become a legend in his own lifetime through his strict devotion to a regime of complete disorganisation. Some said he had taken a master's degree in the subject although Bones himself claimed no higher education than attendance at the school of life. But lack of any formal study had not prevented him from becoming one of the world's finest exponents of putting chaos theory into practice; he was a natural and just did it without thinking; he was capable of laying waste to the best laid plans of mice or men in the blinking of an eye.

"It's him all right and he's brought that great wolf of his with him."

"There's nothing wrong with the dog," said Mike. "In fact, it'd probably play better than you did last week if it got chance."

"Sod off!"

"It's a smashing dog," said Jim. "Loves crisps; do anything for a crisp, that dog."

The coach driver begged to differ about the dog's qualities.

"Dogs are not allowed on the coach," he said

"I've no one to leave him with," declared Bones, "and if he can't come neither can I."

The B team were not to be denied a ten per cent increase in man-power especially when that man was such a vocalist, raconteur and general entertainer as Bones whose combination of versatility and unpredictability made him a rare enough bird to set anyone twitching. To a man they offered the sincerest guarantees of the dog's good conduct. Finally, the driver relented; he was probably thinking,

202

"I'm going to have twenty odd pissed-up rugby players all the way back from Furness. What difference is one dog going to make?" Besides he was a big, handsome dog and he looked almost human. That was more than could be said for some of the other passengers.

"Glad you could make it, Bones. Did you manage to find your boots?" asked the skipper.

"Everything should be in this bag," said Bones, chucking a tattered old duffle bag on to the coach whilst he went back to put the door of the pick-up back on its hinge and fasten it with a piece of string.

"Just check his bag, will you lads," said the skipper as he went to help Bones with the door.

"Yes. He's got some boots. There's more grass on them than on the second team pitch and I don't just mean per square inch. But I think they might just do. He's going to need some laces though; they're absolutely rotten. He's got some shorts ... a jock ... one sock ... no, hang on, there's another one stuffed inside one of his boots ... a pair of waterproof trousers, a woolly hat, a couple of stiff paint brushes, a library book, a bicycle clip and a disgusting, mouldy sandwich but no towel."

"You can't have everything."

"He generally thieves somebody else's towel anyway. We were up at South Hoddersdale and I couldn't find my towel when I came out the shower. I went into the changing room and there's Bones sat on it with his great hairy arse. He's the only bloke I've ever known who puts his socks and shoes on before his underpants. He said he was sorry; my towel looked like one of his. Then he realised his was still in his bag so he offered to lend me that, except it was still wet from the week before."

Bones and dog were jibed aboard and made their way towards the back as the coach set off. One happy result of Bones's chaotic lifestyle was that he had a fund of stories about silly scrapes he had got into and bizarre brushes with the law which just would not have happened to anyone else. Even though it often turned out that the joke was on him he still managed to have a good laugh about it. His bonhomie was infectious and provided the catalyst for one tale leading, as it often does, to another. He also had his own repertoire of songs, making him a one man source of entertainment, roughly half of which was intentional and the other half unintentional. His period of absence had ensured him an even warmer welcome than usual and there was a general expectation in the company that his presence could not fail to enhance the day's proceedings. He was not just a good man to have on such an outing; he had no equal.

When it came to seating on the away coach there was an established pecking order. There were those who always sat at the back of the coach, those who always sat at the front and those without any particular conviction. Quality newspapers might be unfolded at the front whilst playing cards and dirty magazines[72] would feature at the back. Insults and repartee would be traded between front and back but it seemed one of the immutable laws of physics that whilst the porn might go forwards the broadsheets never went backwards.

As it was a long journey some had brought sandwiches for lunch. Despite the early hour these began to be unwrapped before the coach was a mile down the road. The spectators at the various feasts divided into those who tried to scrounge and those who could never eat after breakfast on a match day. If an eater happened to be seated next to a non-eater a brief but pointless conversation inevitably ensued in which the non-eater would express disgust that the other could eat before a match to which the stock reply was an expression of

---

[72] *Apart from illegal imports these were restricted to the exposure of breasts and bottoms at the time. However, the publishers were even then testing the boundaries of what constituted obscenity under the Obscene Publications Act (1959) and the landmark case of "Lady Chatterley's Lover"(1960). I remember one occasion when detailed scrutiny conducted with the aid of a prop's jam-jar bottom spectacles as a magnifying glass produced a lengthy but inconclusive debate as to whether what was visible was shadow or pubic hair.*

amazement that the neighbour could play on an empty stomach. More experienced players saved their breath. The result was similar to that in the other stereotyped conversation which took place on board the coach about pipe smoking. Just as the smoker carried on smoking, the eater carried on eating and the observer in each case continued to be disgusted.

The rustle of paper and the smell of food encouraged Bonzo, Bones's dog to leave his seat at his master's side in order to forage. He was a loyal dog but there were limits. He had been sitting upright peering intelligently towards the front but now reverted to all fours in search of scraps which were in generous supply. Someone had a bag of crisps. Bonzo could hear the rustle of a crisp bag at a hundred paces in a hurricane and he devoted the owner of the bag the whole of his attention until at least ten seconds after the empty bag had been discarded.

The hubbub of the early conversation had begun to die down. Greetings had been exchanged and acquaintances renewed with the Vickers specialists, any news of immediate interest dealt with and any questionable conduct during the previous week's after match activities discussed and, where appropriate, censured in the time-honoured manner:

"You dirty bugger!" or, if the perpetrator was absent,
"The dirty bugger!"

Thoughts were beginning to focus vaguely on the game ahead and a general lull took over. More than the others, the intellectuals at the front were prone to engage in a period of quiet inward reflection whilst the front row forwards, not being equipped with this facility, were apt to doze off. Pablo, being an intellectual by profession, naturally sat at the front of the coach. However, on this particular journey even the more tranquil ambience to be found at the front was unable to calm his irritated frame of mind. He could not avoid reflecting on the situation in which he found himself; he had not expected to be on the coach that day and he did not like it in the least. He had played in the first team last week and the "*Vickers Away*" card had come as a complete shock, particularly as the skipper had made a point of asking him after last week's game about his availability. He had thought that meant his place in the first team was guaranteed. It had almost put him off his bacon butty when the card came on Wednesday morning. In his own opinion he had not had a bad game last week and did not deserve to be dropped. These last few weeks he had had better things to do than go to training although he knew he could do with being a bit fitter. Nevertheless, he thought he had managed to hide himself pretty well amongst the backs on the occasions when he had been struggling to keep up with play. In fact, he had nearly scored on one occasion when he had found himself in the back line: despite a valiant effort on his part he had just failed to hang on to a poor pass - from the skipper of all people. A better pass and he would have scored. The Vale had been pressing hard till then and the position was lost after that but it wasn't his fault. Admittedly, the centre who was outside him had complained loud and long after the game because, for some reason, he thought the pass was intended for him and not for Pablo and he would have been certain to score if Pablo hadn't cocked it up, but then the Fancy Dans in the backs were always whingeing on about something.

A sense of injustice smouldered. He knew he was still a better player than the guy who had displaced him, even if the other bloke was a bit fitter than he was, but now here he was on the bus to Barrow. He would have been a bit more crafty if he had seen that one coming. He had racked his brain ever since Wednesday morning for a plausible reason to cry off but had not been able to come up with one good enough. The demotion on its own was bad enough but he had been looking forward to the disco at the club that night when he was hoping to further his acquaintance with a very attractive young lady who, he was certain, would be there. He had already decided she was nice and thought he was in with a good chance of finding out whether she was naughty.

What was worse he knew he had a rival for her affections who was playing at home. The swine. Come to think of it he was a smooth talking swine as well that Matt Jinks, There was no danger the coach would get back for the disco that night; just about every serious piss-head who had turned out for the club in living memory was sitting at the back. The vote on a late stay was a foregone conclusion; in fact, they wouldn't even bother with a vote. The swines! It had never been known for the coach to come back at a sensible time from Vickers. He should have cried off. But if he had done that without an excuse that sounded completely genuine he knew he would have been out of the first team for a long time; Roy didn't like fishy cry-offs and would have scuppered any chance of an early return to the first team. What a dilemma! He realised now that the first team captain had stitched him up last week by asking about his availability. The swine! Making a show of writing the names down of those who said they were available had all been part of a plot. And he would definitely have to go training next week now. What a bag of! And the first training session wasn't until Tuesday, the day after the selection meeting so his presence there would not be noted till the week after. Shit! And the second team was away next week as well. At some dreary place the other side of Manchester nobody had ever heard of but if he got stuck with this lot of piss-artists they'd probably stay out all night again. The more he thought about his predicament the more it irritated him and he sat there fuming and festering with frustration.

Meanwhile, Bonzo had been obliged, after many a hopeful trip up and down the aisle and unspoken entreaties of all and sundry, to accept that there was no more food to be had and either out of appreciation for what he had just had or disappointment that there was to be no more, unleashed a salvo of barks which suggested an idea to one of the artists at the back; quietly and hesitatingly at first, putting both the metre and his lyrical skills to the test, he began to sing ;-

"One man went to play, went to play at Vickers".
Then more boldly:-
"One man and his dog went to play at Vickers".

The refrain was soon taken up by degrees by all the denizens of the back seats.
"Two men went to play ... "
There are some who always join in,

"Three men went to play..."

Others who can be infected depending on their mood,

"Four men went to play...."

Some who are reluctant initially but join in once it's got going.

"Five men went to play..."

Whilst there may be someone who finds the repetitiveness irritating.

"Six men went to play ... "

And after a while it starts to get on his nerves.

"Seven men went to play ... "

As already observed, Pablo was not in the best of moods.

"Eight men went to play ... "

And the slightly dubious syntax of "eight men and his dog" seemed an annoying challenge to his professional capacity. Was it correct or not? He wasn't really sure.

"Nine men went to play ... "

Bonzo, who somehow sensed he was intimately concerned, chipped in with a couple of joyous barks here and there.

"Ten men, nine men, seven men, six men, five men, four men, three men, two men, one man and his dog went to play at Vickers".

"Yap. Bark. Woof. Yap. Howl." Bonzo seemed to have rounded it off with a fine medley, hitting some surprisingly high notes for a big dog.

"Eleven men went to play ... "

When he discovered that his quite reasonable expectation that the number of men going to play at Vickers would equate to the number who had famously set out to mow a meadow was unfounded and there were eleven and now twelve men setting out on this pastoral adventure with their canine companion, the embodiment of which, in the shape of Bonzo, was now contributing an amazing range of barks, woofs, yaps and howls as his excitement increased, it became too much for Pablo and he began to shout abuse at the end of each verse:-

"Put a bloody sock in it!"

"That's enough for Christ's sake. Shut up!"

"You're all a set of morons!"

And so on.

By the time it ended in a bout of joyful self-congratulation amongst the participants in which Bonzo featured prominently, no less than twenty six men and his dog had gone to play at Vickers and Pablo was thoroughly brassed off and roused enough to shout out,

"Thank goodness that's the end of that, you idiots!"

Almost a full ten seconds elapsed before *One man went to play* started up again, this time even louder, with everyone joining in to the accompaniment of foot stamping. Long before the end of the second rendition Pablo would have been seriously considering violence against his own team-mates had there not been so many of them. But for everyone else the warmth of the ambience had risen by several degrees. The way was open for Bones to relate one or two of the daft things that had happened to him since the last time he had been seen and to tell one or two from his fund of stories all of which whetted the general appetite for more of the same. It was going to be a good day.

The matches went as expected with Vickers victorious in both. However, Pablo in the 'A' team back row took every opportunity to indulge his natural appetite for skulduggery and thuggery, sharpened as it was by the day's events. The final whistle came as a relief to the opposing scrum half and brought with it a narrow victory for the home team. The 'B' team match had been a humdinger; The Vale, having sportingly been lent three of their reserves by Vickers, had managed to cling to a slim lead right up to the final stages. The disappointment of honourable defeat was easily assuaged by a couple of pints so that by 5.00pm equilibrium was restored and all were looking forward to tea, some singing, games, several more pints and whatever other entertainment the evening might have to offer.

Six hours later last orders had been taken and no more ale could be purchased. Some were contentedly aware that they had already had enough, some were incapable of getting any more down their greedy little necks, much as they would have liked to, whilst one or two, who had long since passed the point of no return, were dredging[73] or looking optimistically behind curtains for drinks which they or someone else might have left on the windowsills in anticipation of the very emergency which now presented itself. Those very few at whom Aphrodite had winked were doing their best to consummate their good fortune in the little time that remained for the team captains were beginning the round-up for the long journey home.

Over the course of the evening Pablo had mellowed. He was pleased he had given the opposing scrum half a torrid time which he was sure must have been noted by the second team skipper. He hoped that might help him to get back in the first team next week. He had managed to spend a good part of the evening providing convivial company for his captain upon whom he had impressed his intentions of coming to training on a regular basis in future; he had explained that he had been very busy over the last few weeks with what he had described as 'extra curricular' activities (by which he meant nothing in particular but it sounded good). He had gone round and collected the match fees and made sure that the skipper's pot was kept full as well as his own whenever a jug[74] came round. He was confident he had managed to draw the fine line between subtly ingratiating himself and appearing obsequious. "You never know," he thought to himself,

---

[73] *Dredging was the collection and consumption of the contents of abandoned glasses after closing time. This was not to be confused with ale-snatching which was, of course, a capital offence. Sometimes the line could become a little blurred.*

[74] *Traditionally, the home team always bought the opposition a jug of ale to share round. The away team might buy one back and it could go on from there. More often than not the jug was a chipped, enamelled affair that looked like it belonged in a Victorian washroom.*

"someone in the first team back row might have had a stinker or got injured even or, may be just not available for next week."

Hope springs eternal and is wont to spring even higher after a few pints. He had a feeling he was in with a good chance of getting his place back; by degrees he became sure he had done enough to persuade his skipper of today to put in a good word for him. Perhaps total disaster might yet be averted; he could be back in the first team next week and able to pick up where he left off with the lovely girl he had been chatting up at the last disco. That was assuming, of course, that Matt Jinks hadn't already snaffled the prize but there was always a good chance Matt Jinks's fancy might have been taken elsewhere. He was easily distracted was Matt Jinks. Had it not been approaching midnight the sun might have broken through any second.

Slowly the lads from The Vale were being decanted from the clubhouse into the coach. Some were trying to conceal pint glasses which they had borrowed and which they intended to fill from the stash of tins on the coach. The glasses borrowed would be replaced, more or less, by the ones the Vickers lads were trying to conceal as they left The Vale's clubhouse at a similar time. The Vale captains had looked in all the usual places both inside and outside the clubhouse and were confident that everybody had been rounded up. They were just going back to the clubhouse for the last time to collect the shirt bags and make a final check when Pablo offered,

"Anything I can do, skip?"

The skipper was somewhat taken aback by this offer as he had never previously considered Pablo to be the kind to be in the running for the clubman of the year award. He had been hanging around him all evening; he had hardly been able to go for a piss without him following. Still, to be fair, he had made himself useful. He had had a good game too. They might want him back in the first team next week; with luck the first team skipper wouldn't ask about him but if he did he'd have to think of some good reason for keeping him in his team.

"Er ... Well ... er ... Tell you what. You do the head count will you, Pablo?"

211

"No problem, skip."

"Do you know how many there should be?"

"Twenty bloody six; I could hardly forget."

"OK. Don't forget there's me and Uppard collecting the shirts and don't forget to count yourself," he laughed.

Pablo curbed a strong desire to make some sarcastic remark; to tell him not to insult his intelligence but he was mindful of the selection meeting on Monday. At all costs he must not spoil the good impression he had worked so hard to create at that stage.

Some minutes later, the captains re-appeared behind a couple of stragglers, one of whom was grinning from ear to ear. They looked round the dimly lit coach and asked Pablo if everybody was on.

"With the two you've just brought – and yourselves, of course - that's the lot," he replied.

The captains were relieved. It was bad enough for anybody to be left anywhere at that time on a Saturday night but Vickers, out on the end of the Furness Peninsula, was something else. They felt like they had been in charge for a long day and were keen to be rid of their responsibilities. The good thing was that from now on the audience was captive. The pubs and chippies were all closed and, whilst there would be at least a couple of roadside lavatory stops there was no danger of losing anybody and no need for any more head counts. They could relax. They sat down together and toasted each other with a tin.

The first hour or so of the return journey was fairly lively, interspersed with inevitable choruses of "One man went to play". Even Pablo joined in. (He had managed to convince himself by now that Matt Jinks would have fluffed his lines with the young lady even if he did still fancy her and she would be a certainty to fall to Pablo's own charms next week). But Bonzo would not chip in with any woofs and yaps this time. Deprived of the dog's spirited interventions, as the beer took effect the proceedings gradually diminished to sporadic outbursts from the back. Even these had died out long before the coach approached its destination.

In the dreary hours of Sunday morning the coach did a circular tour of the conurbation from which The Vale drew its players, dropping off its passengers in small groups here and there within staggering distance of their homes. Finally, it arrived to deposit the final residue from whence it had come at the club car park. There were only three remaining of the twenty six who had set out. Two dragged the shirt bags into the changing rooms at the now darkened clubhouse whilst the skipper went to ring his wife from the nearby phone box to ask her to come and collect them as he had arranged previously. They waited outside the clubhouse, oblivious to the chill.

"Where's Bones?" asked the skipper, suddenly, reminded by the sight of the old pick-up. "I promised to get him home if he turned out for us."

"He must have got off."

"Couldn't have done. We didn't go anywhere near where he lives."

"Well, you know what he's like. He probably fancied his chances of knocking on some lady friend's door."

"Yeah. Ever the optimist. The Lord loves a cheerful trier."

"But there's not many women do at this time in the morning."

"Mind you he looked like he was getting close to a result with that lass with the long hair and short skirt he'd been plying with drink all night. Vickers has always been one of his happy hunting grounds."

"Well, it's strange he's not here but I'm sure the dog was still on the coach just before we got off."

"Couldn't have been. Not here now is it? You're bloody pissed."

"Course I'm pissed. But I'm sure the dog was on the bus. It was sitting next to me at one time, looking out the window."

"Loves crisps, that dog," slurred Jim. "Sit next to anybody with a bag of crisps."

"So where was Bones then if the dog was next to you? It always sits with him."

" 'less somebody's got a bag of crisps," muttered Jim. "S'nice dog that; loves crisps."

"Will you shut up about the bloody crisps, Jim. We're trying to work out what's happened to Bones. I thought he must have been crashed out on the back seat."

"No. That corpse was Jim here. Wasn't it, Jim?"

"What?"

"It was you, wasn't it?"

"What was?"

"Oh, forget it! Anyway Bones isn't here and neither is the dog so they must've got off somewhere."

Any further speculation was interrupted by the return of the coach which rounded the corner into the club car park at speed to be greeted by a mocking cheer.

"Hey up! This'll be them now. Bones and the dog. Like I said Bones'll have been asleep, pissed-up somewhere on the back of the coach. The driver'll've found him and brought him back."

"Will you come and get this bloody dog off," said the driver, "so I can go home and get some sleep."

" Is Bones on there as well?"

"What? Look , I don´t know whether it's got his bloody bone or not. Will you come and get it off. It won't move for me. It's gone half past sod-all already and I want to get home and get some sleep."

"No. I didn't mean has the dog got its bone; I meant . . ." the skipper's voice trailed off as he realised the futility of trying to explain it all and he decided life was too short.

"Never mind. Come on lads," he shouted. "It looks like we'll have to go on and carry Bones off."

They spotted the dog straight away; they could hardly miss him; he was sitting upright near the back, peering at them over the rows of seats. But of Bones, comatose or otherwise, there was no sign, neither on nor under the back seat, nor anywhere else.

"This is bloody strange," said the skipper. "I don't understand how this can have happened. I know Bones is a walking disaster zone but even he wouldn't have got off and left the dog."

"The dog wouldn't have let him anyway. Would've followed him. Grand dog, that," said Jim.

"That's right. So where is Bones then?"

"He can't have got off."

"I agree but if he couldn't have got off was he ever on?"

"Must've been. Pablo did a head count; saw him doing it."

"So if Bones got on and he didn't get off where the hell is he?" said the skipper, completely baffled.

It was a bit late at night for the Agatha Christie stuff. He began vaguely to look round the coach again as if hoping Bones might suddenly re-appear out of nowhere by some kind of magic. His eyes alighted on Bonzo who was still sitting there on his haunches on one of the seats and, as he looked, Bonzo turned two sorrowful eyes on him. He could have sworn the dog was trying to tell him something. In the half light he almost looked almost human. Then, suddenly, he shouted,

"Bloody hell! I know what's happened: it's that dozy bugger Pablo. He's gone and counted the dog!"

As greatly concerned as they were about Bones's predicament, many miles from home without a toothbrush but highly probably with a cash-flow problem, I would be lying if I said there was not even the slightest giggle at his expense.

"He must have been pushing his luck at the death with that bird he was chatting up and missed the bus. But what about the dog? How come it got on without him?"

" It'll follow anybody with a bag of crisps, that dog," said Jim.

"It's all Pablo's fault. What a pillock ! Fancy counting the bloody dog!"

"I'm not surprised. His eyesight goes after he's had six pints; you should have seen that woman he was trying to get off with at the disco last week."

" Was she rough?"

"Rough? Rough? Ruff ! Ruff! Ruff! Rauooool!"

Bonzo turned to look but, missing his master, was not inspired enough to join in.

"Can't have been that bad; Pablo said Matt Jinks was chatting her up as well."

"Matt Jinks? You're joking. He was just winding Pablo up."

"Was she really that rough then?"

"As rough as a rhino's knackerbag."

"I'd no idea his eyes were so bad."

"He normally wears glasses except when he's playing or on the prowl."

"She'd big tits though. He wouldn't have needed his glasses to clock them."

"'n any case," said Jim, "was'n easy mistake fr'im to make; 's a good looking dog is Bonzo - better looking than what Pablo usually ends up with."

"You really like that dog don't you, Jim?" asked the skipper.

"Yeah. 'reckon's' nice dog."

"Good. Then you can take him home and look after him till Bones gets back. I hope you've got plenty of crisps in."

POST-MATCH DE-BRIEF

That's the end of the story
There isn't any more
There's an apple up my arse
And you can have the core
Singing roll tiddly o shit or bust
Never let your bollocks dangle in the dust.

Congratulations! Unless you have cheated, which, unfortunately, unlike in the good old days, can no longer be ruled out, you have managed to last the whole match. It would be unfair not to mention that Bones arrived home safely late the following day. Being a gentleman of the old school, he would never say where he had found a berth for the night but the first thing he did when he got back, so as to be sure he didn't forget, was to put a cheque in the post to the youngish lady who had kindly lent him the rail fare. He posted the cheque on his way to collect Bonzo from Jim who had pushed a note through his letterbox much earlier in the day. Jim's wife did not share his enthusiasm for the large dog's company and his head was in no condition to withstand the punishment his ears were getting. So we'll hear no more of Bones, Jim, Pablo, the skipper, Gordon, Sicky, Wilf, Badger, Ben, Jimmy and the many others – at least not in this book. The funny thing is I cannot remember any of them ever retiring from playing rugby. Certainly, there was never any announcement. I know they must have stopped playing at The Vale at some stage because there came a time when I realised that it was years since I last saw them in their kit. It's impossible to think of them playing anywhere else yet when I go to other clubs to watch a match I'm sure I catch the odd, fleeting glimpse of them on the field and hear their voices somewhere in the background in the bar afterwards. If it's not them it must be someone very much like them. And when I look at the team photographs in other clubhouses – as you do sometimes when you're waiting for someone else to get the beer in – many a time I have to get my glasses out just to make sure that the player on the left of the back row in the photograph with the awkward stance wasn't actually Jim, or that one with the mischievous grin wasn't Bones, standing next to Pablo with the raggy tash or it wasn't Gordon who was doing the old chest out, stomach in routine.

The observant reader will have noticed that not only is this book split into two halves but that I didn't come out to play after half-time. I have no doubt this was a much bigger disappointment for me than it was for you or, for that matter, anyone else, apart, possibly, from that big centre who used to play at Hoddlesdale and who was really looking forward to playing against me again. However, the memory of the enjoyment of my playing days will always be with me. How could I ever forget? The knackered knee, the missing teeth, the sharp twinge in the neck if I turn my head too quickly to the left are daily reminders of all the fun I had. It's perhaps a good job my playing career did not last long; there could have been so many happy reminders I might not have been able to get out of bed in the morning for thinking about them. But, of course, despite my loss the game went on and goes on.

Whilst I soon learnt that there is no substitute for playing - you really feel you've earned that pint afterwards – and despite many changes in the game I suspect that I am with almost everyone else who ever played, in believing it is still the only game in town; the ambience just does not exist elsewhere. Once invited to write a piece for a magazine produced for a certain club's jubilee celebration, G. A. MacIntosh, then President of the Lancashire Rugby Football Union, who, like many others, followed his playing career with years of unpaid service to the amateur game, wrote that "the real meaning of rugby was to make friends both on and off the field".

Despite the unlikelihood of the proposition that eighty minutes should be spent attempting to fulfil a mutual intent to knock seven bells out of each other simply in order to make friends, we all know just what he meant. However, that part of the game which takes place on the field provides only the introduction to lasting friendship; it obviates the need to ask, how are we, what do we do, where do we live and other polite irrelevancies. Actions speak louder than words and there will be plenty of time for talking later in the bar which is where the friendships are actually cemented. That brings me to another of life's little mysteries, chicken and egg type, which I have not been able to solve: was the social side the result of having enjoyed the game so much that we did not want to go home or did we put up with being battered around all Saturday afternoon because we had so much fun afterwards? Soccer is not troubled with this conundrum. In my experience soccer players are quite happy to turn up, play the game and even if they do not then go straight home they do not usually – although exceptions prove every rule – go to a bar with members of the opposing side. However, in rugby the bar is absolutely indispensable: even if a club is not fortunate enough to have its own clubhouse with a bar it will have an arrangement with a nearby hostelry. (If anyone knows of a temperance rugby club please let me know). Like it or not, and mostly we do like it, rugby and bars cannot be disentangled the one from the other. The drink, of course, is beer: bitter normally, lager possibly, stout sometimes. Medical opinion seems to be divided about the optimum daily dosage and sometimes suggests it may be possible to have too much of a good thing. (At The Vale we always drank responsibly but rugby, like most English institutions, is a broad church and at the other end of the scale you might find a club like Colbourne where drinking to excess was the norm). In the greater scheme of things these are but a minor details; the basic principle could not be clearer: the bar is where the bonding takes place and the beer is the essential bonding medium.

Whilst the bar is indispensable for the current player it is also a great thing for the retired player/spectator. When visiting another club he immediately feels at home, if not exactly his own home then one belonging to a close friend or relative. Whilst he may go in not knowing anyone it is unlikely he will leave without making at least one acquaintance who will be pleased to share a pint or two with him on his next visit.

As the bar is the focal point of the camaraderie it is the place where the tales of derring-do are told and the third major ingredient, humour, comes into the rugby mix. In a typical post-match scene there

219

are several old duffers standing at the bar, a couple from one club and the rest from the other. They've had a pint or two. One throws into the conversation,

"Our lot are playing Old Toehillians next week and . . ."

Before he can finish a bloke from the other club butts in,

"Old Toehillians! We used to play them!" and turning to his clubmate continues,

"Do you remember that time when Bill Rosthorne got up to do the Muffin Man and he ... and he ... "

"Never forget it," chimes in the other. "He was just going to ... and he ... and he ... he ..."

And they are both shaking so much they have to put their beer down on the bar. Tears start rolling down their cheeks and the rest of the story becomes completely unintelligible. The guys from the other club haven't a clue what happened really but they know it must have been hilarious so they adopt big silly grins in sympathy. Then it's their turn.

"Talking about the Muffin Man, do you remember when old Jimmy Youngs had just got to the final stages at Bletcherdale when those two nuns walked in and ..."

"It wasn't at Bletcherdale: it was at Little Norton."

"You're right, come to think of it. It was at Little Norton. Very similar clubhouse. Anyway he had just got to the final stages when they walked in and he said ... he said ... and ..."

Now the both of them are convulsed with laughter whilst the sympathetic silly grins pass to the other side. If you are listening in you want to know what the hell two nuns were doing at Little Norton Rugby Club on a Saturday evening but forget it: you are never going to find out. You just have to put on a silly grin and think about what you can come up with as your contribution. Over the years these stories have been told and re-told so many times that they have been stripped down to only the bare essentials required to jog the memory; they are reproduced in a kind of shorthand which can only be fully understood if you were there or if you are fully familiar with the characters and places involved. It's like the sketch in "Porridge"[75] which I will describe in detail for the benefit of the younger reader: the jailbirds are all standing around and when someone shouts out a number they fall about laughing. Someone else shouts out another number and the same thing happens. The new inmate, naturally, wants to know what is going on. Ronnie Barker's character explains that they have all heard the jokes so many times before that they know them off by heart and all they need to remember a joke is the number it has been given.

It is said that beauty lies in the eye of the beholder but in rugby tales the humour lies in the collective memory of the listeners. It's difficult to enjoy a humorous reminiscence on your own (and if you are successful you're likely to get locked up) but I hope that these tales have stirred some happy memories of your own and that you have had as much fun reading this book as I have had writing it. If that is the case and in the unlikely event that you feel you may have had more than your money's worth or, in the more likely event that you are a generous soul, please remember the Rugby Football Union Injured Players Foundation. Should you feel disposed to make a donation you will find the details on the opposite page.

---

[75] *British situation comedy broadcast on BBC1 from 1974 to 1977, running for three series and starring Ronnie Barker and Richard Beckinsale as two inmates at the fictional HMP Slade in Cumberland/Cumbria.*

By purchasing this copy of **The Mud the Beer and the Rugby** you have already made a small contribution to the foundation as £ 1 from every copy sold is donated to the Foundation. Every little does help. If you wish to make a donation of your own or to get involved in fundraising please visit

www.rfu.ipf.org.uk